Discovering
THE UNIVERSE

[*Frontispiece*]   Man has always been impressed by the splendour
of the heavens, and primitive Man soon discovered the relation
between certain groups of stars and the seasons. The heavens
became peopled with legendary characters, many of the legends
became widespread and have survived as names of the
constellations to this day. This illustration is of the celestial globe
of Coronelli, 1693, dominated by Hercules grasping the Serpent.
To the left is Libra (the scales or balance), and above the
Serpent's head is the crown (Corona Borealis).

Discovering
THE UNIVERSE

A.C. BERNARD *and* JOYCE LOVELL

HARPER & ROW, PUBLISHERS

New York and Evanston

PREFACE

THE RADIO TELESCOPE at Jodrell Bank which is now such a familiar feature of the Cheshire plain was born at the same time as the first Russian Sputnik. In that remarkable autumn of 1957 an avalanche of people and telephone calls descended upon us and there often seemed little distinction between day and night, or between the site of the telescope and our own home three miles away. The life which we knew before October 1957 has never quite returned. In the first few years about a quarter of a million people wrote to ask if it was possible to see the telescope and hear about its work. Perhaps a quarter of these inquiries have come to us privately as a family. At that time, in the absence of any official organisation to deal with visitors, we did our best to meet these private approaches.

During the course of this unofficial activity we have found that in trying to understand the work of the telescope our visitors have many difficulties in common. In this book we have tried to explain the work with which the telescope is associated in the way we have often used with these visitors. The degrees of understanding vary widely. The rather elementary, fundamental differences, between optical and radio telescopes often have to be explained to people who appreciate, even if they do not fully understand, the far more difficult problems of cosmology. So it is with this book. It is not a textbook, and it is certainly not a book for specialists. We hope it will have an appeal to all ages like the giant which we see from our own garden.

M.J.L.
A.C.B.L.

CONTENTS

1 The development of astronomy

ASTRONOMY IN THE ANCIENT WORLD

From the time of the earliest civilisations Man has studied the movements of the heavenly bodies, and from his observations has gradually built up ideas of his own place in the structure of the universe. Primitive Man, watching the rising and setting of certain groups of stars, created many legends associated with them, and peopled the heavens with characters bearing both good and evil influences upon his own activties—seed-time and harvest, birth and death—and these stories were passed down by word of mouth. The constellations, or groups of stars, received names from Greek mythology and an astronomer returning from the centuries before Christ would recognise many of the names still used for the constellations in the Northern Hemisphere in the twentieth century A.D. Upon the various influences of the constellations on Man's activities, Virgil writes in the first book of the *Georgics:*

> What makes the cornfields happy, under what constellation
> It's best to turn the soil, my friend, and train the vine
> On the elm, the care of cattle, the management of flocks
> The knowledge you need for keeping frugal bees—all this
> I'll now begin to relate.[1]

The sailor depended upon his knowledge of the constellations for navigation:
'It was with a happy heart that the good Odysseus spread his sail to catch the wind and used his seamanship to keep his boat straight with the steering-oar. There he sat and never closed his eyes in sleep, but kept them on the Pleiades, or watched Boötes slowly set, or the Great Bear, nicknamed the Wain, which always wheels round in the same place and looks across at Orion the Hunter with a wary eye. It was this constellation, the only one which never bathes in Ocean's Stream, that the wise goddess Calypso had told him to keep on his left hand as he made across the sea.'[2]

A document of the constellations devised by Eudoxus (409–356 B.C.), one of the oldest we have, shows the earth at the centre, with the interlocking spheres of the sun, moon and planets moving around it. This earth-centred, or geocentric, view of the universe was to persist for many centuries, and indeed until long after the introduction of improved measuring techniques began to challenge all Man's previous theories of the structure of the universe in which he lived.

[1] Translation, C. Day Lewis   [2] HOMER's *Odyssey*, Bk. V, Translation, E. V. Rieu

Meanwhile in 230 B.C. it was a Greek astronomer who measured the circumference of the earth, using two observers to measure the angle between a given star and the zenith, as it crossed their meridian at a certain time and place. Attempts were made by Aristarchus of Samos (*c.* 270 B.C.) to measure the size and distance of the sun and moon, and by the beginning of the first century B.C. Hipparchus had made a list of the positions of over a thousand stars, as well as measuring the precession, or circular swing, of the earth's axis.

Ptolemy's theories of the movements of sun, moon and planets, each revolving round a circle of its own, with the earth immovable at the centre of the universe, were set out in *The Almagest*. In this work he divided the stars into six classes of brightness (magnitude), a star of the 1st magnitude being 100 times as bright as one of the 6th. His views conflicted in no way with the Aristotelian philosophy accepted by scholars in which Man on earth was fixed at the centre of a universe composed of the four elements: earth, water, air and fire. There was little challenge to his views for many centuries, and it was through the work of Copernicus (1473–1543) that the next great surge forward in astronomical knowledge came. He assumed that the earth rotated on its axis and that the sun was at the centre of the universe, so that each year the earth and planets moved around it, whilst the moon moved round the earth. This heliocentric (or sun-centred) theory was finally printed just before his death in the famous document entitled 'Concerning the revolutions of the Heavenly Spheres'.

ASTRONOMY IN THE SIXTEENTH AND SEVENTEENTH CENTURIES
He was followed by Tycho Brahe (1546–1601) from whose observations (made possible by his remarkable development of measuring instruments) tables of planetary orbits were devised, whilst the great mathematician Kepler (1571–1630) worked out the laws governing the movements of the planets, and showed that their true paths were ellipses and not circles. It was in 1610 that Galileo, having heard of a magnifying instrument made in Flanders, in which two lenses were put together in such a way as to make distant objects seem larger and nearer, looked through his small new telescope and observed the mountains on the surface of the moon, the sun's spots and Jupiter's moons. The lens was barely an inch in diameter, but from this moment astronomers had a tool of investigation in their hands, incomparably more powerful than any they had possessed before, and tremendous advances in their knowledge of the universe were now made possible, though not without opposition from those to whom the new theories upset old beliefs.

Sir Isaac Newton's experiment in 1676 showed that sunlight passing through a prism was composed of seven colours and directed his attention to the reflecting type of telescope of which he presented the Royal Society with a small model. Modern astronomy has developed on the basis of his great law of universal gravitation: that the force of attraction between two bodies is proportional to the product of their masses and inversely proportional to the square of their distance apart. For nearly two thousand years the theories of Aristotle had proved unassailable, but now at last astronomy was breaking free, for the vital link with tradition had been severed.

DEVELOPMENT OF THE OPTICAL TELESCOPE
IN THE TWENTIETH CENTURY

Ever since the introduction of the first telescope 350 years ago, it was realised that with an increase in the size of the instruments so there would be a corresponding increase in the depth to which they could penetrate into space. After the work of Lord Rosse in the eighteenth century and Herschel in the nineteenth century, who built telescopes of increasing size and power in Britain, it was in America that the great advances in this field occurred in the twentieth century. The 100-in. telescope on Mt Wilson was first used in 1918, and the 200-in. on Mt Palomar thirty years later.

Then Man's ideas about the size and organisation of the universe were challenged as never before, and beliefs which had been held for centuries could no longer be substantiated in the light of the new knowledge which these telescopes brought to the astronomers. Hitherto, Man, looking up at the system of stars, visible on a clear night, known as the Milky Way, imagined it to be confined in space and representing the whole of the universe. He thought that the sun, earth and planets were at the centre of this system, with the sun, a typical star, appearing bright because it was close to him. The stars, on the other hand, were faint because they were far away. He believed, until observations were made with the new telescopes, that many thousands of millions of stars in the Milky Way system were distributed in a more or less spherical enclosure, across which it would take a ray of light, travelling at 186,000 miles per sec., a few thousand years to traverse.

NEW IDEAS ABOUT THE STRUCTURE OF THE UNIVERSE

With the use of the new instruments it became clear that the stars of the Milky Way, numbering about 100,000 million, were arranged asymmetrically in a flattened disk across which it would take a ray of light 100,000 years to travel. The stars appeared to be concentrated in spirals, radiating from the centre like a giant octopus, whilst the earth, by no means being found at the centre of this disk, was situated far out on one of the spiral arms, 30,000 'light-years' from the centre.

In describing the distances separating our solar family from the stars and nebulae in space we use the expression 'light-years', this being the distance which a ray of light travels in a year. The speed of light is 186,000 miles per sec., the light from the sun takes 8 minutes on its journey of 93 million miles to earth,

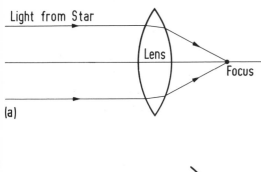

(a)

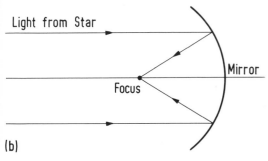

(b)

[*Left*] The two principal types of optical telescope. (*a*) The refractor in which a convex lens is used to change the beam of parallel rays from a distant object such as a star into an image at the focus. This lens is the objective. The image which it forms at the focus is inverted, but this is not a drawback in astronomical work. The image formed by the objective at the focus is viewed through a magnifying glass (the eyepiece). This refracting telescope was invented either by the Dutch spectacle-maker Hans Lippersley in 1608, or by the Italian della Porta of Naples. It was the instrument first used by Galileo in the early seventeenth century for astronomical observations.

(*b*) In the reflecting telescope a spherical or paraboloidal mirror is used to bring the parallel rays from the star to form the image at the focus which is then viewed with a lens eyepiece. This type of telescope was first developed by Newton. Large modern telescopes are nearly all of this reflecting type. The largest refracting telescopes are those at the Lick Observatory, with a lens of 36 in. diameter, completed in 1885, and at the Yerkes Observatory, with a lens of 40 in. diameter, completed in 1895. These large lenses have to be so thick that the absorption of the light in passing through them begins to outweigh the increase in the amount of light collected from the star, and it is for this reason that the large modern telescopes are giant versions of Newton's original reflecting telescope.

[*Right*] Newton's reflecting telescope which he presented to the Royal Society in 1671. The mirror is only 1 in. in diameter, the focal length 6 in. and the magnifying power 38. A hundred years later in 1789 William Herschel built a reflecting telescope with a mirror of 48 in., and the telescope made by the Earl of Rosse in the nineteenth century had a mirror of 72 in. diameter.

therefore we say that the sun is 8 light-minutes away. The light from Pluto, a few thousand million miles away, takes 6½ hours, whilst our distance from the nearest star is so great that its light takes 4½ years to reach us.

Hence we must realise that our astronomical knowledge is nearly all of time past. Our knowledge of the sun is 8 minutes old, and of the nearest star 4½ years out of date, whilst the light from some of the stars in the Milky Way has taken 100,000 years on its journey towards us, and the light from the nebula in the constellation of Andromeda 2 million years.

From this position far out in one of the spiral arms of our galaxy we, on earth, are unable to see the nucleus (the central regions) of the galaxy because of obscuration by the dust which exists in interstellar space. This dust obscures the view from the telescopes and shuts out more than 90 per cent of the light of the stars, whose radiance otherwise would be as bright as that of the moon. It is only through the development of radio telescopes that Man has been able to penetrate this dust to study the detailed structure of the central regions of the Milky Way.

The large optical telescopes revealed that the Milky Way itself is only a local galaxy, and the distances separating the stars within it are minute compared with those separating the galaxies themselves. Herschel observed a faint nebulous patch in the constellation of Andromeda 150 years ago, and speculated whether this and other similar hazy patches might lie outside the Milky Way, but he was unable to produce conclusive evidence and these nebulae were believed to be in the Milky Way.

The Mt Wilson telescope was powerful enough to resolve the nebulae into stars, and the evidence showed indeed that Herschel's speculation was right, and that there were other galaxies of stars at vast distances from the Milky Way system. The light from the Andromeda nebula reaching the telescopes today has been travelling through space for 2 million years, and comes from another stellar system, similar in size and content to our own Milky Way.

[*Opposite*]   A drawing made by Russell W. Porter of a sectional view through the dome of the world's largest optical telescope— the 200-in. Hale telescope on Mt Palomar in California. The sky was first viewed through this telescope in December 1947. The mirror weighs 14½ tons and the whole telescope 530 tons. The friction is so small that a ½ h.p. motor can turn the entire instrument. The alternative arrangements for viewing the image formed by the 200-in. mirror are shown diagrammatically in the accompanying sketches.

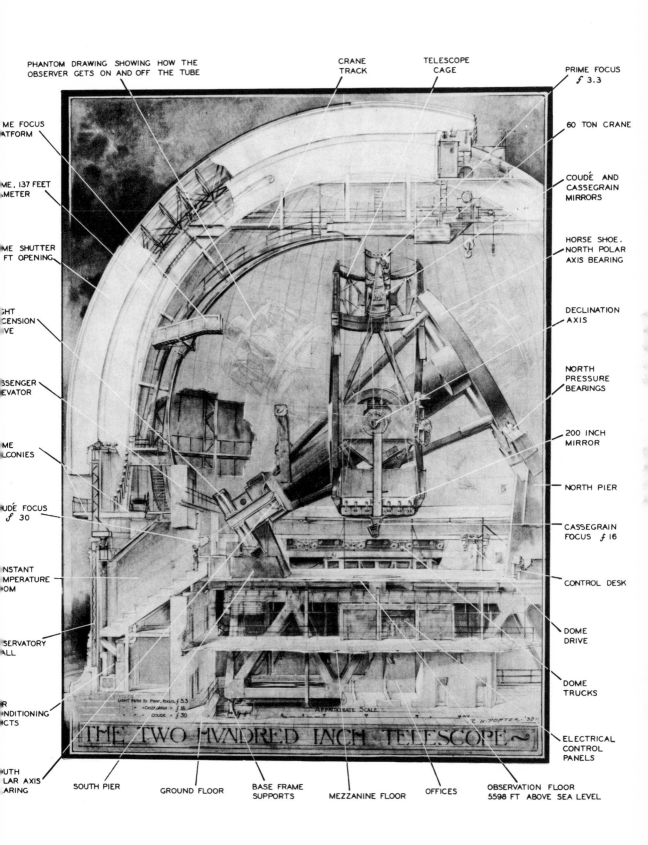

PHANTOM DRAWING SHOWING HOW THE
OBSERVER GETS ON AND OFF THE TUBE

CRANE
TRACK

TELESCOPE
CAGE

PRIME FOCUS
ƒ 3.3

ME FOCUS
ATFORM

60 TON CRANE

ME, 137 FEET
AMETER

COUDÉ AND
CASSEGRAIN
MIRRORS

ME SHUTTER
FT OPENING

HORSE SHOE.
NORTH POLAR
AXIS BEARING

GHT
CENSION
VE

DECLINATION
AXIS

SSENGER
EVATOR

NORTH
PRESSURE
BEARINGS

ME
LCONIES

200 INCH
MIRROR

UDÉ FOCUS
ƒ 30

NORTH PIER

NSTANT
MPERATURE
OM

CASSEGRAIN
FOCUS ƒ 16

CONTROL DESK

SERVATORY
ALL

DOME
DRIVE

R
NDITIONING
CTS

DOME
TRUCKS

LIGHT PATH TO PRIM. FOCUS ƒ 3.3
CASSEGRAIN ƒ 16
COUDE ƒ 30

APPROXIMATE SCALE

R. W. PORTER '38

THE TWO HVNDRED INCH TELESCOPE

ELECTRICAL
CONTROL
PANELS

UTH
LAR AXIS
ARING

SOUTH PIER

GROUND FLOOR

BASE FRAME
SUPPORTS

MEZZANINE FLOOR

OFFICES

OBSERVATION FLOOR
5598 FT ABOVE SEA LEVEL

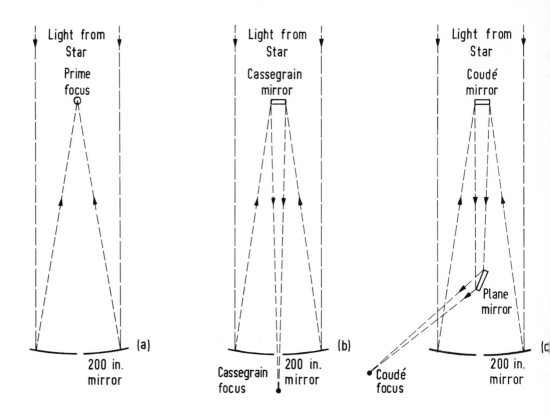

(a), (b) and (c) show three alternative optical arrangements for viewing the image formed by the 200-in. mirror. (a) is the straightforward case where the image is viewed or photographed at the normal (prime) focus. The observer can be carried at this focus in a cage when the telescope is in operation. The focal length is 55 ft. If it is desired to obtain a larger image the focal length can be increased to 226½ ft. by the arrangement shown at (b). A small convex mirror is mounted in front of the prime focus, and this reflects the light through a hole in the centre of the main 200-in. mirror to a position outside the telescope tube. The small mirror is known as the Cassegrain mirror, and the focus behind the main mirror is the Cassegrain focus. An even larger image can be obtained by increasing the focal length to 500 ft., using the Coudé arrangement shown in (c). Here the small mirror in front of the prime focus reflects the light back down the axis of the tube, where it is intercepted by a plane mirror, orientated to reflect the image outside the telescope tube, to the Coudé focus. As an example, the image of the disk of the moon has a diameter of 6 in. in the arrangement (a), 28 in. in (b) and 53 in. in (c).

The use of the Cassegrain and Coudé foci have other advantages in that heavier and more bulky equipment can be used at the focus, since it will be outside the telescope tube and will not obscure the light from the stars. In the case of the Coudé focus the plane mirror is arranged to reflect the light outside the telescope tube along the polar axis, so that the Coudé focus is stationary with respect to the motion of the telescope tube. Permanent and extensive photographic or other recording equipment can therefore be installed in this position.

The two basic methods of mounting and guiding a telescope (either optical or radio). In the alt-azimuth mounting at (a), the telescope can be rotated independently about a vertical (azimuth) axis and horizontal (elevation) axis. In order to follow a star or other stellar object the telescope has to be moved simultaneously in both axes, and this needs accurate automatic computing and driving equipment. The large radio telescopes (see Chapter 2) are driven in this way, but the system is rarely used for large optical telescopes because it is difficult to achieve the extreme accuracy of guidance which they need by this method. In these cases the equatorial, or polar axis, mounting shown at (b) is used. With respect to an observer on earth the motion of the stars appears to be circular, centred on the north celestial pole. Thus if the main polar axis of the telescope is mounted to point at the north celestial pole, a single rotation of the telescope around this axis at the appropriate rate will keep it trained on the star or other object in the heavens. To change the field of view of the telescope (that is, to look at stars at different declinations farther away from the pole) the telescope can be rotated (and then fixed) around an axis at right angles to the polar axis (the declination axis). The 200-in. telescope and the 48-in. Schmidt telescope illustrated here are mounted in special versions of the basic arrangement shown at (b).

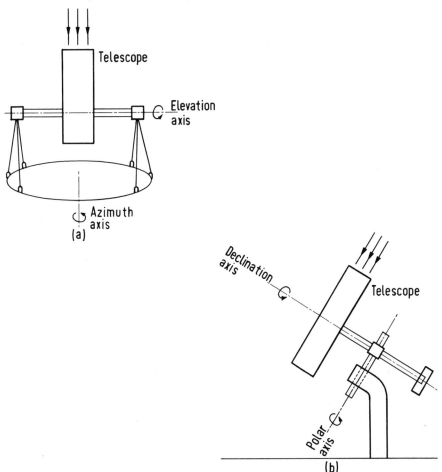

A modern high-precision optical telescope—the 48-in. Schmidt-type telescope on Mt Palomar. The observer is at the guiding eyepiece. The optical arrangements of this type of telescope (see accompanying diagram) were devised by B. Schmidt of Bergedorf in 1930 and are effectively the combination of a refractor and reflector telescope which gives excellent definition over a wide field of view. The telescope illustrated can photograph a relatively large area of sky (e.g. 5°×5°) in a single exposure. It was used to compile the famous *National Geographic Society—Palomar Observatory Sky Atlas*. For this the telescope took 1,758 photographs between 1949 and 1956 and the *Atlas* has become one of the most important reference catalogues of the sky for astronomers.

Through the use of these large optical telescopes Man has learnt that the galaxies exist in great groups or clusters, and just as the earth and planets are bound to the sun and move together through space, so on a vaster scale the galaxies are contained in clusters as connected physical systems. The galaxies within the clusters are in random motion under their own gravitational attraction. The expansion of the universe is manifested by the recession of the clusters of galaxies from one another. As we recede into space the rate of expansion always increases. At the limit of the present-day penetration of the optical telescopes the clusters are moving away from us at a speed of over 80,000 miles

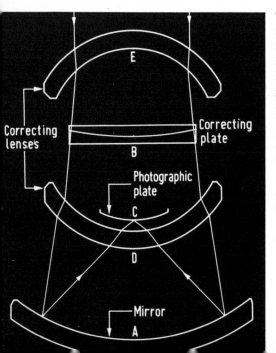

The basic arrangement of the lenses and mirror in the Schmidt type of telescope. The original system devised by Schmidt consisted of a concave spherical mirror (*A*) and a glass correcting plate (*B*) in front of it. The mirror has a large aperture and short focal length in order to give good sensitivity over a large field of view. However, such a mirror has aberrations which would give an image too poor for astronomical work. These aberrations are neutralised by the nearly flat plate (*B*). The photographic plate (*C*), which has to be curved, is placed at the focus between the plate and the mirror. The system was modified by Baker in the United States in 1947 to give even greater fields of view without distortion. These 'Super Schmidts' included additional correcting lenses (*D*) and (*E*) to reduce the aberrations at large angles from the axis of the mirror.

16

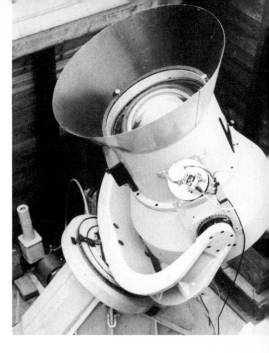

A small Schmidt camera-telescope in use at Jodrell Bank. The aperture is 12·9 in. and the field of view 56°. This camera was built according to the principles of the Super Schmidt, shown in the accompanying diagram, specifically for the photography of shooting stars or meteors (see Chapter 7). These meteors occur infrequently and the maximum sky coverage compatible with good sensitivity is essential. This camera also included an 18-bladed rotating shutter in the focal plane. By rotating this at high speed the image of the meteor trail was occulted at a known rate and the velocity of the meteor could be measured. The effect is shown in the meteor photograph in Chapter 7.

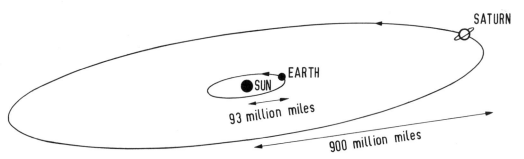

Mass of Earth = 6,000 million million million tons
Mass of Saturn = 570,000 million million million tons

Newton's universal law of gravitation applies to the forces governing the motion of the stars and planets as much as to the falling of the apple from the tree on earth. He discovered that the force of attraction between two bodies is proportional to the product of their masses and inversely proportional to the square of the distance between them. For example, consider the earth and the planet Saturn moving in their orbits around the sun. Saturn is just over ninety-five times heavier than the earth, and if they were situated at the same distance from the sun, then according to Newton's Law the attraction between Saturn and the sun would be ninety-five times greater than that between the earth and the sun. But Saturn is moving in an orbit just under ten times farther away from the sun than the earth's orbit, and because of this the force of attraction is decreased by nearly one hundred times. Thus the inverse square of the distance roughly counterbalances the fact that Saturn is so much heavier and consequently the gravitational forces of attraction between the earth and the sun, and between Saturn and the sun are about the same.

17

per sec. Within 20 minutes of reading this the distance separating us from these distant galaxies will have increased by more than the 93 million miles which separates the earth from the sun.

This is the broad picture we have been able to build up with the help of the modern astronomical instruments. In subsequent chapters we shall see how some of these exciting discoveries have been made and how our ideas are constantly changing.

[*Opposite*] The great spiral nebulae in Andromeda (M31), photographed with the 48-in. Schmidt telescope at Mt Palomar. This nebula is 2 million light-years distant from our own Milky Way system and we believe that it is similar to the Milky Way and that our own system would appear like this if photographed from the Andromeda nebula. There are about 100,000 million stars in the nebula, and their flattened spiral arrangement is well shown. The light from a star at one extremity of the spiral takes about 100,000 years to traverse the nebula—although travelling 186,000 miles per second. If it were possible to photograph the Milky Way system from such a distant part of the universe, our own spiral structure would be apparent and the sun, with the earth and planets, would be situated in a spiral arm about 30,000 light-years from the central regions of the galaxy.

2 The new tool – Radio astronomy

RADIO WAVES FROM SPACE

It appeared that these big optical telescopes were to be the ultimate means through which Man could obtain information about the stars and galaxies; that is, by observing the light which they emitted. He had evolved with eyes sensitive to the visible part of the spectrum in the range of wave-lengths which lie between the ultra-violet and infra-red, and it is over this region that a transparency exists in the earth's atmosphere. As the wave-length of light moves towards either the red or blue part of the spectrum it becomes increasingly scattered and absorbed by the water vapour and dust in the atmosphere.

When viewed from earth the sky appears blue because of this scattering of sunlight—the astronauts move above these scattering regions and for them the sky appears to be black. For wave-lengths much shorter than the ultra-violet we move into the region of soft X-rays and these rays which come from the sun are absorbed by other processes high up in the ionosphere as we shall see in Chapter 3. If Man had evolved with eyes sensitive only to infra-red or ultra-violet, then he would have had very little knowledge of outer space until the present day, when it has become possible to move beyond the obscuring regions of the atmosphere with satellites and space probes.

It seemed impossible that Man's knowledge of outer space could ever be accumulated in any part of the spectrum other than through this visible gap, owing to the obscuring effect of the earth's atmosphere on any radiation lying outside the familiar colours of the rainbow. However, early researches with radio waves in the 1920's had revealed another transparency, at much longer wave-lengths, in the radio wave region. Whereas wave-lengths of visible light are measured in millionths of a centimetre, the radio waves in this other transparency in the atmosphere, extend from a fraction of a centimetre to many metres in wave-length. In the central region of this band broadcasting and television transmissions are made on earth.

Although the existence of this transparency was known, it seemed unlikely that it could be of any use to astronomers. The stars and sun are hot bodies, with surface temperatures of many thousands of degrees, and the fundamental laws of physics indicate that their maximum output of energy lies in the visible, or near visible, regions of the spectrum. It was therefore with amazement that astronomers heard in 1931 and 1932 that an electrical engineer, Karl Jansky,

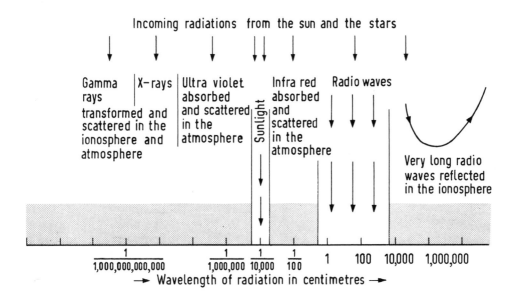

Incoming radiations from the sun and the stars

| Gamma rays transformed and scattered in the ionosphere and atmosphere | X-rays | Ultra violet absorbed and scattered in the atmosphere | Sunlight | Infra red absorbed and scattered in the atmosphere | Radio waves | Very long radio waves reflected in the ionosphere |

$\dfrac{1}{1,000,000,000,000}$ $\dfrac{1}{1,000,000}$ $\dfrac{1}{10,000}$ $\dfrac{1}{100}$ 1 100 10,000 1,000,000

→ Wavelength of radiation in centimetres →

The light which we see with our eyes is only a small part of the electromagnetic spectrum. For example, X-rays and radio waves are fundamentally of the same nature as light; their characteristics differ because their wave-lengths are different. Whereas the wave-length of light is measured in terms of ten-thousandths of a centimetre, the wave-length of radio waves is much longer, and those used in television have wave-lengths measured in metres. On the other hand, X-rays are of much shorter wave-lengths—measured in hundred-millionths of a centimetre. All these radiations travel through space with the same speed: 186,000 miles per sec., and most of them are incident on the earth from space, but are absorbed or transformed in the earth's atmosphere. There are two transparencies where the radiations come through the atmosphere unimpeded—one in the visible light part of the spectrum and the other in the radio part of the spectrum as shown in the diagram.

had detected some radiations or signals in this part of the spectrum, whose origin, he was convinced, lay in regions of space outside the solar system.

Jansky was working for the Bell Telephone Laboratories in America and had been given the job of finding out the causes of the atmospherics and disturbances which spoilt the long-distance telephonic and radio communications in which his company was interested. His apparatus worked on rather a long wave-length between 14 and 20 metres, and the aerial consisted of an array of rods which could be rotated on a brick foundation. He made the simple and interesting observation that even when there was no obvious cause of atmospherics such as a thunderstorm, there was a residual noise in the equipment which varied throughout the day. It had a regular diurnal variation, and Jansky made the

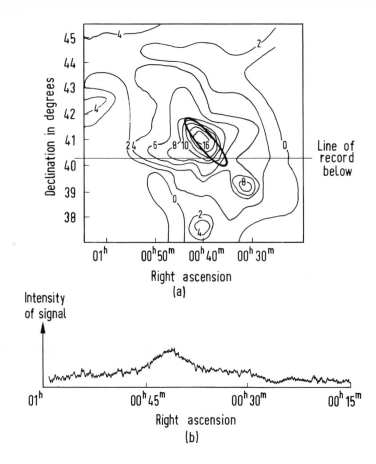

Right ascension
(a)

Intensity
of signal

Right ascension
(b)

The method of building up a radio picture of the sky is illustrated at left. In this particular experiment the Jodrell Bank telescope was used to investigate the radio emissions from the extra-galactic nebula in Andromeda M31. The basic information appears on a pen recorder chart which draws out the variation in strength of the incoming signal as the telescope beam is scanned across the part of the sky containing the nebula as shown at (b). Many hundreds of such records are needed to build up the contour map of isophotes shown at (a). The numbers on the lines indicate the relative strength of the signal on that contour. The actual record at (a) was obtained by moving the telescope so that it crossed the nebula along the line at declination 40° 15′ shown in (b). The increase in signal strength as the telescope beam traverses the nebula is clearly shown between right ascension 00ʰ 30ᵐ and 00ʰ 45ᵐ. The telescope was then readjusted to scan at another declination until a complete mosaic could be plotted. The nebula as photographed in the optical telescopes (page 19) is superimposed in (a) as a heavy line. Obviously the radio waves come not only from the nebula but also from a considerable area surrounding it where the photographs do not reveal any stars. The explanation for this is given in Chapter 8.

classic observation that the maximum in this signal occurred 4 minutes earlier each day. This led him to conclude that the source of the interference, or radio noise, must be coming from regions of space outside the solar system. (A sidereal day consists of 23 hours 56 minutes, which is the period of the rotation of the earth with respect to the stars, not to the sun.) His conclusion that the source of the radio noise had its origin not merely in extra-terrestrial space, but in extra-solar space, has never been doubted, and has become of the utmost importance to development of astronomical studies. At the time, astronomers took little notice of Jansky's discoveries, and the directors of his laboratory instructed him to get on with another job.

22

The simplest form of radio telescope is a parabolic reflector of sheet metal which reflects the incoming radio waves from space to the focus in the same way as the optical telescope reflects the light to the focus. In the optical case the image is viewed through an eyepiece at the focus; in the radio case the radio waves are concentrated on a rod dipole (like a simple television aerial) at the focus, which is connected by cable to the receiver and recording instrument. There are many other versions of radio telescopes which do not have a simple analogy with the optical case. For example, the area equivalent to the parabolic reflector can be built up by large numbers of rod dipoles suitably connected, but although cheaper these types of radio telescopes are rather specialised because they are not easy to steer and are limited to a single wave-length of operation. In telescopes like the one at Jodrell Bank, which uses a parabolic sheet reflector, the operating wave-length can easily be changed by altering the 'primary feed', or the dipole, at the focus. The definition, or beam width, depends on the wave-length divided by the diameter of the reflector. Thus for a given paraboloidal diameter, if the wave-length is doubled, the width of the beam in which the telescope receives will be doubled, and the definition in the radio map will be worsened.

Until the Second World War, development of the subject was left to an amateur, Grote Reber, who built the prototype of the modern radio telescope in the garden of his home in Illinois. This consisted of a bowl, 30 ft. in diameter, in the form of a paraboloid, mounted so that it could be directed to any part of the sky. This telescope has recently been re-erected as a museum piece at the entrance of the U.S. National Radio Astronomy Observatory at Greenbank, West Virginia.

Grote Reber with his radio telescope, re-erected as a museum piece at the entrance to the United States National Radio Astronomy Observatory, Greenbank, West Virginia. The diameter of the reflecting bowl is 30 ft. and the primary feed is held at the focus on the tripod legs. This is the instrument which Reber built in the garden of his home at Wheaton, Illinois, and with which, working as an amateur in his spare time, he confirmed Jansky's discovery of the radio emissions from space and made the first radio map of the sky.

23

By exploring with this instrument the radio waves from the Milky Way, Reber was able to make the first real map of the radio sky with a reasonable degree of precision. Of course, the radio signals received from space by a radio telescope give no information about the distance of the objects from which the signals come. Sometimes, as we shall see later, a radio telescope is used as a radar instrument in which case radio waves are transmitted from it, and then it is possible to time their journey, to and from the moon for example, and to measure the distance of the astronomical object accurately. But this radar technique is limited in astronomy to the nearer objects in the solar system. Normally the radio telescope is used as a receiver only and therefore the radio astronomer's map of the sky is one in plan only. This greatly increases the difficulty of interpreting the results in terms of the stars and galaxies which we recognise in the optical telescopes.

Jansky's conclusion that the noise in his receiver was the result of emissions in the radio part of the spectrum picked up from outer space, was confirmed, and Reber was able to show that the strength of this radio noise depended on the direction in which the beam of his radio telescope was pointing. He found that when he directed the beam, a few degrees wide, towards a region of the sky where the common visible stars were most plentiful, then his signal strength was greatest. On the other hand, when he pointed it to the regions of the Milky Way, where the stars were less concentrated, then the signal strength decreased.

This seemed to be the result one might have expected and led to the conclusion that the stars we see with our eyes in the visible part of the spectrum also emit radio waves. However, when Reber directed his telescope towards some of the brighter stars, such as Sirius or Capella, expecting strong radio emissions, he found none at all. Thus the paradox was established and is still not completely resolved, that although there appears to be a close relationship between the intensity of the radio waves and the regions where there are most visible stars, yet when looked at individually, there is no simple relationship. Even today, apart from one or two doubtful cases, nobody has yet succeeded in detecting radio waves from the individual or common stars in the Milky Way.

The sun, however, is a very strong radio source, so strong that it may hinder the observations of more distant signals, in the same way in which its light renders the stars invisible in optical telescopes. In spite of this, Reber failed to obtain any radio emissions from it, for during his investigations the sun was in a 'quiet' period; that is, a time when sun-spot activity was at its minimum, and, as Sir Edward Appleton and Dr Hey showed after the Second World War, the sun-spots and flares on the solar surface were associated with great and irregular increases in solar radio emissions. These eruptions were frequently accompanied by terrestrial events such as the aurora borealis and fade-outs in transatlantic radio communications. Subsequently it was discovered that radio waves were also detectable from the solar corona, the highly tenuous region of the sun extending far beyond the photosphere, which is the disk of the sun usually seen, and that when the sun was quiet, or undisturbed by spots, then the radio waves were much less intense and came predominantly from this region.

Because he could not detect radio waves either from the sun or the stars, Reber concluded that the source of the waves he was receiving must lie in the regions of interstellar hydrogen gas. After the war, when localised radio sources or 'radio stars' were discovered, this conclusion was disbelieved, but as we shall see in Chapter 8, Reber was partially correct.

THE DEVELOPMENT OF THE RADIO TELESCOPE

The use of radar in the Second World War meant that there was a tremendous incentive to develop equipment of a sensitivity and excellence surpassing anything hitherto available, and as soon as scientists could return to peace-time activities, and use the new techniques to study radio waves from the heavens, instead of locating enemy aircraft and shipping, then it was possible to search for the answers to some of these problems, which had sprung from that first discovery of Jansky in 1931.

The problem of the radio astronomer was the same as that of the optical astronomer: an increase in the size of his instruments was needed for the same reason that larger optical instruments were needed. The optical instrument required a large mirror to collect the maximum light ensuring further penetration into space and good definition. Similarly, increased size was needed with the radio telescope, where radio waves had to be collected over a large area to improve the weak signal strength of emissions generated far out in the cosmos, and also because the resolution of the beam for a given wave-length depended directly on the size of the telescope.

Accordingly, plans were formulated for the building of larger and larger radio telescopes, and the instrument at Jodrell Bank, with a parabolic bowl 250 ft. in diameter, was completed in 1957. No other steerable radio telescope of this size has yet been built. This was specially designed to be stable in high winds; the bowl is mounted so that it can be directed with precision to any part of the sky, and it can be used both as a transmitter and a receiver over a very wide range of wave-lengths. At the moment, the only other fully steerable radio telescope which approaches the Jodrell Bank instrument in size is the telescope at Parkes in South Australia. This is 210 ft. in diameter and was opened in the autumn of 1961 in the Radio Physics Division of the Council for Scientific and Industrial Research.

The Americans intended to build one 600 ft. in diameter at Sugar Grove, West Virginia, but they encountered so many difficulties that it was abandoned in 1962 after £18 million had been spent on it. The Russians appear to be operating a steerable 140-ft. telescope in connection with their deep space tracking network. There are many steerable parabolic telescopes 50–100 ft. in diameter in various countries. Some of these have been built specifically for tracking deep space probes.

THE JODRELL BANK TELESCOPE

The paraboloidal bowl is made of 80 tons of sheet steel, mounted on a cradle, itself weighing 800 tons, whilst the whole structure is suspended on trunnion bearings 185 ft. above ground. Incoming radiation is reflected from this bowl on to the primary feed which is mounted on a mast at the focus, $62\frac{1}{2}$ ft. from the apex of the paraboloid. Electronic apparatus transforms and records the signals received from any part of the sky to which the telescope is directed. For any given wave-length this instrument possesses eight times the definition obtained by Reber's original telescope and sixty-four times greater gain. At the suggestion of Professor Blackett, the 15-in. gun-turret racks, 25 ft. in diameter, of the *Royal Sovereign* battleship, which was dismantled after the war, were used to drive the bowl in elevation; thus it could be tilted to the required angle. The 185-ft. towers supporting the elevation bearings and motors are connected by a diametrical girder at ground-level, pivoted at its centre point, the only place at which the structure is fixed to the ground. The two towers, each carried by six bogies, move at a speed up to $\frac{3}{4}$ m.p.h. on a double railway track 350 ft. in diameter and accurate to $\frac{1}{16}$ in. so that the instrument can be given rotation or movement in azimuth. The moving superstructure weighs 2,500 tons.

A small laboratory hangs beneath the bowl, suspended so that it always remains upright whatever the tilt of the bowl. This contains receiving equipment and is approached along catwalks. Sometimes an observer may wish to

The Jodrell Bank radio telescope is the largest fully steerable parabolic reflector in the world. There are a number of radio telescopes which cover a larger area, but these are specialised instruments and cannot be pointed to any part of the sky. The parabolic bowl of sheet steel is 250 ft. in diameter and the aerial at the focus is carried on the steel mast rising $62\frac{1}{2}$ ft. from the apex of the paraboloid. The control of the telescope is carried out from a building at the left of the photograph. It can be rotated in azimuth on the railway track which is 350 ft. in diameter. The bowl is driven in elevation through the battleship gun-turret racks shown in another photograph. These are mounted on the towers 185 ft. above ground.

The reverse of the bowl showing the 800-ton steel cradle which supports it. The hoop-like semicircular girder is a stabilising device to damp any tendency of the bowl to oscillate in high winds. Large pneumatic wheels are forced against it hydraulically. These can be seen in the photograph mounted on top of the base diametral girder. This photograph also shows the laboratory which is pivoted underneath the bowl, and the catwalks which lead to it from the tops of the towers. Access to these catwalks can be obtained only when the bowl is in the zenithal position, but the observer can remain in the swinging laboratory during operation of the telescope if necessary.

operate equipment in this laboratory with the bowl tilted. A system of automatic safety devices keeps him locked inside the laboratory when the position of the bowl would make it unsafe for him to leave.

In order to avoid losses in cables it is sometimes necessary to mount the receiving equipment close to the primary feed at the focus. A 6-ft. cube box is fixed at the top of the aerial tower, access to this being obtained by a hydraulic platform from the base of the bowl. Inside the box the first stages of the receiving equipment are mounted, and for some work at high frequencies the aerial itself, which may be a horn as distinct from the common rod dipole, emerges directly from this box.

Particularly heavy and large equipment, used in tracking the American Pioneer V, 23 million miles out into space, was recently removed with the help of a helicopter, so that the steel plates of the bowl itself need not be taken out. The accompanying picture shows the unusual sight of people standing in the bowl when it was tilted away from the zenith (*see page* 33).

[*Below*] This photograph was taken in April 1956 and shows how the bowl of the telescope was constructed. By the autumn of 1956 the main framework was completed, supported at that stage on 90 miles of scaffold tubing. The central hub of the bowl is clearly shown here; the swinging laboratory hangs immediately below this.

The reflecting membrane is made up of 7,000 steel sheets, each about 3×3 ft., $\frac{1}{12}$ in. thick, specially shaped to fit on to the steel purlins to which they are welded.

The $62\frac{1}{2}$-ft. aerial tower rising from the apex of the paraboloid, photographed during the final stages of its erection. Dipoles are in position at the top of the tower. After experience in using the telescope, a 6-ft. cube box was mounted on top of this tower so that some parts of the receiving equipment could be placed close to the aerial. This box can be seen in the photographs of the completed telescope.

The two towers of the telescope are each mounted on six bogies. The central two in each case are driven by 50 h.p. electric motors to give the rotation in azimuth. The remaining eight bogies, four under each tower, are not driven—these are the wind carriages. Each bogie runs on four steel rollers, tapered to allow for the curvature of the rails.

The bowl is driven in elevation through two 25-ft. gun-turret racks from the *Royal Sovereign* battleship. The circular housing of these racks near the tops of the towers can be seen in some of the other photographs.

[*Below*] One of the two trunnion bearings which carry the bowl. The housing of the battleship gun-turret rack is immediately behind the trunnion. The hole in the bearing is to allow the cables to pass through to the equipment on the bowl.

There are no slip rings on the telescope, since it is important to avoid danger of sparking or bad contacts which would give interference. Special arrangements therefore have to be made for the large number of cables so that they will not be broken or strained when the telescope is moved. This shows the 'cable twisting' arrangement at the entrance to one of the holes through the trunnion bearings. A much larger cable twister is used over the central point on the base diametral girder since, in addition to the cables for the apparatus, the main power cables come on to the telescope at that point. The telescope rotates through 360° plus a 60° overlap and must then be reversed, otherwise, even with the cable twister, the cables would be snapped. Special safety devices are included to prevent this happening.

A view from a catwalk of the region where the bowl is supported on the tops of the towers. The circular housing is that of the battleship gun-turret rack.

From his desk in the control room of the telescope, 200 yds. away, the controller can command the instrument to perform any motion required by the experimenter. It may be driven separately in azimuth and elevation, whilst a sidereal motion may be obtained by driving through a computer in right ascension and declination. Under these conditions the position to which the telescope has to be directed is worked out by the computer, it will then follow automatically a given star from rising to setting, or the sun or a planet, depending on the needs of the research programme.

The control room of the telescope from which all its motions are controlled. The instrument may be driven separately in azimuth and elevation or through a computer to give automatic sidereal motion in order to follow a star or other astronomical object. Reading from left to right, the groups of three dials show, on the left, galactic latitude, galactic longitude, sidereal time, right ascension, declination; on the right the required azimuth, the required elevation, Universal Time (G.M.T.), the actual azimuth, and the actual elevation of the telescope.

Whereas the records of the optical telescope appear on a photographic plate or in the form of spectrographs, the records of the radio telescope appear as an ink trace on a paper chart. This shows the strength of the signal in relation to the time and position of the telescope beam. It is necessary for the investigation of even one single object, such as the M31 nebula in Andromeda, to obtain many hundreds of these records, with the telescope scanning over different parts of the nebula, so that a mosaic may be built up. This system of isophotes gives the radio picture—the equivalent of the optical astronomer's photograph.

The process of building up the mosaic of isophotes from the hundreds of ink charts is a lengthy operation, and it may take a group of two or three people many months to analyse records which they have obtained in a few nights of work with the telescope. Recently the output of the receiving equipment has been fed on to punched tape, as well as to the pen recorders. The analysis of the tape in a high-speed computer may be carried out in a few hours, although of course a considerable time is taken to prepare the 'programmes' for the computer.

[*Opposite*] A helicopter removing a load of apparatus from the bowl. This was the transmitter which was used to command the space probe Pioneer V.

The top section of the 62½-ft. aerial tower which, rising from the apex of the paraboloid, carries the primary feed aerial at the focus. The focus lies in the plane of the aperture of the bowl the rim of which can be seen in this photograph. The box at the top of the tower holds the early stages of some of the receiving equipment on the high frequencies where it is essential to avoid losses in the feeders. The aerial itself can either be mounted from the tower top, or as shown in this illustration, from the bottom of the box. Access can be obtained either on the open ladder on the right of the tower or by the hydraulically operated platform which is carrying the observer to the focus for adjustments of the apparatus.

3 Scientific instruments in space

THE FIRST ARTIFICIAL EARTH SATELLITE

Telescopes, radio telescopes and, on 4 October 1957, the Russians demonstrated that scientific instruments need no longer be earthbound by launching Sputnik I. With the possibility of escape from the obscuring layers of the earth's atmosphere into regions outside, these new instruments could be used to study incoming radiations and particles in the planetary system before they were absorbed or distorted by the earth's own atmosphere.

Newton had suggested that a body might be sent from the earth's surface, and become a miniature moon, or artificial earth satellite, which would follow a definite path and be subject to the same laws which govern celestial bodies. He pictured the problem in the following way. Imagine a mountain so high that there is no atmosphere to interfere with the rocket's motion: a rocket launched from its summit at a certain speed would follow a high arched course and fall at a distance from the mountain. Double the speed and range and the trajectory flattens out. Now if the rocket is given a speed so that the curvature of its trajectory coincides with that of the earth's surface, it will go round the earth and continue to circle it. This then is the minimum velocity at which a body circles but does not fall back on the earth. When a body moves in a circle a centrifugal force arises which is proportional to the square of the velocity. So the speed of the body circling the earth in the vacuum of outer space will remain constant, as the gravitational force is balanced by the centrifugal force acting in opposition.

Newton's diagram picturing an artificial moon. He imagined a mountain so high that the air no longer interfered with the motion of a projectile. Then a projectile, shot horizontally from the top of the mountain, would fall to earth at (*A*). If the speed of the projectile is doubled, the trajectory will flatten out and it will fall to earth farther away at (*B*). Eventually, if the projectile is given a velocity such that the curvature of the trajectory (*C*) coincides with that of the earth's surface, then it will go entirely around the earth and continue to circle it.

34

Now, 250 years after Newton's suggestion, the first tiny satellite, released from its carrier rocket, began to circle the earth, and his idea of a miniature moon had at last been achieved. It seemed appropriate that the Jodrell Bank radio telescope, barely completed, was able to detect the carrier rocket by radar when it was over a thousand miles away.

The Sputnik consisted of a sphere 23 in. in diameter weighing 184 lb. The body was made of aluminium alloy, and its surface was machined and polished to make it more easily visible. It was equipped with small radio transmitters, operating on frequencies of 20 and 40 Mc. per sec. (that is, wave-lengths of 15 and 7·5 m.). The transmitting aerials consisted of four rods, each about 8 ft. long. These lay flat during the firing of the rocket, but afterwards were extended when the protective nose cone was released. They were the only parts outside —all the instruments and power sources were placed inside the body, which was hermetically sealed and filled with nitrogen.

The main classes of orbits for vehicles launched from earth with increasing velocity. At (A) a satellite can be established in a nearly circular orbit a few hundred miles above the earth if the launching velocity is 25,000 ft. per sec. As the velocity of launching increases, the orbit becomes increasingly elliptical as at (B) and the greatest distance of the satellite from earth (the apogee) increases. When the launching velocity reaches 36,700 ft. per sec. the ellipse opens to the parabola (C), the borderline case between the closed ellipse and the open hyperbola at (D), which is the orbit taken by vehicles launched with speeds exceeding 36,700 ft. per sec., in which case the vehicle escapes from the primary influence of the earth's gravitational attraction into interplanetary space.

Many years of work in the development of rockets lay behind this launching. Although weapons described as rockets were used by the Chinese during the thirteenth century in the Battle of Pien-King and probably resembled fire arrows which terrified rather than injured the enemy, it was not until the seventeenth century that we have records of serious attempts to achieve rocket flight. Blaise Pascal demonstrated in an experiment on the Pûy de Dôme mountain that an increase in altitude entailed a decrease in atmospheric pressure, the important inference from this being that if Man wished to devise a method of travelling through space, then it must be by a means of propulsion able to function in a vacuum.

Cyrano de Bergerac suggested the use of rockets for this purpose, and from that time we have drawings and descriptions of rockets of many kinds, with the addition, in the seventeenth century, of stabilising fins. They were heavily encased in iron to withstand the high pressure caused by the burning of powder fuels, and were advocated and used for military purposes. A Russian school-master, Tsiolkovsky (1857–1935), first demonstrated in a scientific thesis that the presence of air is not necessary for the operation of a rocket, and he introduced the idea of liquid fuel. The thrust was to be provided by ejected gases —the more fuel consumed and the greater the velocity of the gases being ejected, the faster the rocket would move. As a result of this there was no longer any need for the heavy iron casing, and the prospect of reaching far greater altitudes than ever before seemed possible.

Sputnik I—the world's first artificial earth satellite launched from Russia on 4 October 1957. Compared with modern satellites and space probes, Sputnik I was small and simple. The small sphere contained transmitters which gave the familiar 'bleep-bleep' in the receivers on earth, enabling it to be tracked, and also giving information about the temperature and other factors inside the sphere. Launched originally in an orbit which extended at apogee to 587 miles from earth and approached to 135 miles, the Sputnik circled the earth for 92 days before burning up in the atmosphere. The carrier rocket which launched the Sputnik burnt up in the atmosphere on 1 December 1957.

36

An American, Dr Goddard (1882–1945), set out to produce a rocket in which the main fuel supply was separated from the combustion chamber. The rate of flow was regulated by pumps delivering the fuels to the chamber, where by chemical reaction they burnt, thrusting the rocket forward by recoil. The liquids he finally chose were petrol and liquid oxygen, and in 1926 the first liquid fuelled rocket was successfully fired at Auburn, Massachusetts, travelling 184 ft. at an estimated speed of 60 m.p.h. Dr Goddard's pioneer work has been recognised by the National Aeronautics and Space Administration (NASA), who have named their great establishment just outside Washington, D.C., the 'Goddard Space Flight Center'. It was ten years before Goddard's reports were published, and in subsequent firings both a barometer and a camera had made successful ascents. This work inspired others in the same field and a means of gyroscopic control was introduced to stabilise the rocket's course. Greater altitudes were reached, and water-cooling of the chamber made it possible for higher temperatures and pressures to be allowed. The steady advance continued until the pace of development was dramatically increased by the militarists' demand for new weapons of destruction in the Second World War.

Three stages in the development of the modern launching rocket: (a) 1926 Dr R. H. Goddard, the American pioneer with the first liquid fuelled rocket which travelled 184 ft. at a speed of about 60 m.p.h.; (b) 1944 the V-2 rocket with which the Germans bombarded London. It reached a height of about 60 miles; (c) 1960 a modern American rocket in process of launching a space probe towards the moon from Cape Canaveral.

The German 'buzz-bomb' or V-1 had a range of nearly 200 miles, and the fuel supply could be cut off by a mechanism at the required moment, where-upon the bomb fell to earth. The engine contained a tube screened by flaps, or shutters, which were forced open in flight admitting air under pressure, the petrol was ignited and the resultant explosion closed the shutters and fuel valves, and released a stream of gas from the exhaust nozzle. The pressure having been relieved, the flaps opened, admitting more air, more fuel ignited, and so on.

The far more powerful V-2, designed by Werner von Braun, was flown successfully in 1942, and climbed to a height of 60 miles. German workers found substitute fuels to take the place of liquid oxygen, which with a boiling-point of only 183°C. presented tremendous storage problems. A variety of rocket-driven devices were developed, and plans to extend the range to 350 miles by fitting wings were interrupted by the ending of the war.

Very soon after the end of the Second World War, however, the desire of the militarists to be able to deliver an atomic bomb by means of a rocket led to a new and intense drive on the development of these ballistic rockets. Dr Werner von Braun became head of one of the development teams in the United States. Although no details were available of the Russians' activities, there were insistent rumours in 1957 that they had perfected a ballistic rocket with a range of several thousand miles. In August of that year newspaper reports stated that such a rocket had actually been tested over Soviet territory.

So far none of these rockets had sufficient power to gain a high enough launching velocity, enabling the rocket to escape through the earth's atmosphere and circle the earth in space. But to those in close touch with these problems it seemed, during the summer of 1957, that the Russian rocket, which could send a heavy bomb over a distance of several thousand miles, might have enough power to give a small and light payload sufficient velocity to place it in an orbit around the earth. The dramatic news of the launching of the Sputnik on 4 October showed that this was indeed the case.

Less than a month after this first launching, Sputnik II, weighing 260 lb. and carrying an animal (the dog Laika) and instruments, was sent up. This included equipment for studying solar radiation in the ultra-violet and X-ray regions of the spectrum, as well as cosmic rays, temperature and pressure. The air-tight container in which the dog was placed contained food, instruments for studying life processes in space and measuring instruments, whilst the wireless transmitters operated on the same frequencies as before.

The developments in America were pressing hard on those in Russia, and after some unsuccessful attempts to launch the Vanguard satellites, success was achieved on 31 January 1958, when Explorer I was placed in orbit by a rocket developed by Dr von Braun's team. Explorer I weighed 31 lb., and this was soon followed by the launching of further Explorer satellites and the 'grape-fruit' satellite Vanguard I, so called because of its small size and weight (14 lb.). In fact, the disparity between the size and weight of the satellites which the Americans were able to place in orbit, and those launched by Russia, was underlined by Sputnik III.

Launched in May 1958, Sputnik III weighed 1,327 lb. It contained radio-telemetering apparatus which memorised the data and relayed it to earth as the satellite passed over special stations, designed to receive the accumulated information. It had a programming device which ensured automatic functioning of the apparatus, and the power supply was obtained by using solar cells to convert the sun's rays into electrical power. Sputnik III was designed to investigate a wide range of problems, including those associated with the earth's magnetic field, and radiations in space.

THE ORBIT OF AN EARTH SATELLITE

In space flight the path or orbit of a satellite is determined by the gravitational attraction of concentrated masses of material and the laws of motion discovered by Newton. The earth and planets of our solar system are so nearly spherical in shape that, for the purpose of calculating the approximate orbit of a satellite, they can be considered to have a force of attraction like that of a single mass point at the centre of a body. This means that their satellites move either in:

(i) an elliptical orbit, or

(ii) a hyperbolic orbit.

The path of the first is closed, and will be repeated time after time (earth satellite) and that of the second is open, and extends to infinity (moon or Venus probe). There is also a third type or orbit (iii), the parabolic, which is the borderline case between (i) and (ii). In all these orbits the velocity is greatest at the nearest point of approach to the parent body, and least at the most remote points. An interplanetary rocket, having overcome the pull of the earth and 'escaped', then loses speed, but on entering the gravitational field of another planet or the moon, picks up speed and begins to fall towards it.

The type of path taken by a space vehicle depends on its speed. A take-off velocity of 36,700 ft. per sec. (7 miles per sec.) is needed to establish a parabolic orbit, and this speed is called the 'escape velocity'. If the vehicle reaches this speed, or exceeds it, then its path will be an open one, and escaping from earth, it will travel farther and farther into space, and will become an artificial planet in orbit around the sun. (Unless, of course, it is directed to collide with a planet, or go in orbit around a planet.)

If this speed is not achieved then the vehicle will remain in the earth's neighbourhood in a closed elliptical orbit. To estimate the necessary speeds two factors must be considered:

(a) Distance from the centre of the earth to the space vehicle.

(b) Mass of the earth.

The escape velocity increases as the square root of the planet's mass, and decreases as the square root of the distance from the centre of the planet. So a rocket must achieve a speed of 36,700 ft. per sec. to escape from the earth's surface, whilst to escape from the moon the speed need only be 7,800 ft. per sec. For Venus the required speed is 33,600 ft. per sec., for Mercury 13,600 ft. per sec., Mars 16,700 ft. per sec. and for Jupiter 197,000 ft. per sec. The time taken to make a full circuit is called the 'period', and its length depends on the mass of the parent body and the major axis, or distance across the orbit at its greatest width. As the major axis increases, the period is longer, and the more massive the parent body, the lesser the period.

In order to establish a body as an artificial earth satellite it must be given a velocity somewhat below the escape velocity. The required velocity depends on the distance at which the satellite is to orbit the earth. If the altitude is to be a few hundred miles, the velocity required is about 25,000 ft. per sec., and the orbit will be almost circular around the earth. As the velocity is increased the path of the satellite around the earth will become increasingly elliptical, and the apogee, or the most distant part of the orbit, will move farther away from the earth. If the apogee is in the neighbourhood of the moon —240,000 miles from earth—then the velocity with which the rocket must leave the earth is only slightly below the escape, or parabolic velocity of 36,700 ft. per sec.

If a satellite is launched at such a distance from earth that it actually moves in the near vacuum of interplanetary space, then, apart from accidental collisions with meteorites, it will stay in orbit for ever, or at least for many tens of thousands of years. Some of the space probes, which have escaped the primary influence of the earth's gravitational attraction, are now in orbit around the sun and come into this category. However, the earth satellites are not moving in such conditions of near vacuum, and at the nearest point of their orbit to earth (the perigee) they receive a slight drag or retardation. Although the earth's atmosphere is highly attenuated at a distance of one or two hundred miles from its surface, its cumulative effect eventually causes the satellite to lose altitude and eventually spiral into the denser regions of the atmosphere, where it burns up. The average satellite is close to its final descent by the time its orbit has shrunk to the stage of taking only 88 or 89 minutes to circle the earth. In the case of the heavy manned satellites, like the Vostoks, the periods have been about 88·5 minutes, but because of their weight they are immune from dangers of early re-entry, and retro-rockets have to be fired to decrease the speed when the return to earth is desired.

ROCKETS OF THE FUTURE

The rockets carrying these first satellites away from the earth were developed into composite, or multi-stage rockets, having a first stage, which when exhausted falls away, whereupon the second stage rocket is fired. There may be a third stage which sometimes remains attached to the scientific payload, and in some advanced forms of space rockets this stage has reserve fuel which can be burned on command from earth in order to give small increments of speed—or to retard the rocket. By this means more precise adjustments of the orbit can be made, which is of particular importance in probes designed to approach the moon or the planets.

Although the rockets now under development, and expected to be available in a few years, will have sufficient power to take men to the moon, nevertheless there is a constant search for new forms of propulsion other than the chemical

The basic problem of the orbit of a space vehicle to the planets is determined by the fact that before launching the vehicle is moving with the earth's velocity around the sun—100,000 ft. per sec.; and that the vehicle must be fired with a velocity greater than the escape velocity from earth—36,700 ft. per sec. If the vehicle is fired in the *same* direction as the earth's orbital motion around the sun, then its independent velocity around the sun will be greater than that of the earth's, and the vehicle will take up an orbit such as (A), farther from the sun than the earth's orbit. This is the type of launching necessary to inject vehicles into orbits which will carry them to the outer planets, Mars, Jupiter, etc., and the *minimum* launch velocities are given in the text. If a vehicle is fired in a direction opposite to that of the earth's motion around the sun, then its independent velocity around the sun will be less than that of the earth's and the vehicle will take up an orbit like (B), closer to the sun than the earth's orbit. This is the type of launching necessary to reach the inner planets—Venus and Mercury. The necessity to cancel out the predominant effect of the earth's orbital velocity means that it is almost as hard to reach Mercury as it is to propel a vehicle to Jupiter. More details of the various types of possible orbits are given in Chapter 5.

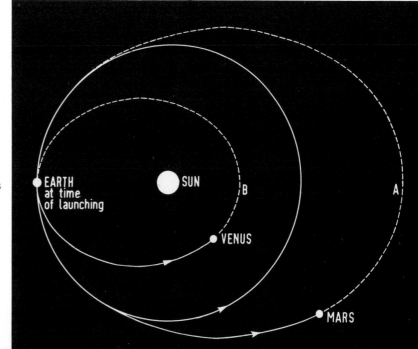

fuels which are now in use. The extra power is required to lift even heavier loads into orbit, or to carry a constant power source when the vehicle is already in space in order to increase the velocity of travel. The latter is particularly important when planetary missions are involved. For example, the minimum launching velocity from the earth and the transit time to reach the planets are as follows:

Mercury	44,000 ft. per sec.	110 days
Venus	38,000	150
Mars	38,000	260
Jupiter	46,000	2·7 years
Saturn	49,000	6
Uranus	51,000	16
Neptune	52,000	31
Pluto	53,000	46

When a launching velocity from earth of 54,000 ft. per sec. is attained the space vehicle escapes, not only from the earth, but from the solar system as well. Its orbit is a parabola with the sun at the focus, and the vehicle would move out of the solar system into interstellar space, where after aeons of time it might come under the gravitational influence of another star. For any missions beyond Venus or Mars it is clear that some extra thrust, capable of development when the rocket is actually in space, is highly desirable. For this reason new forms of

The technique of placing a satellite in orbit is as follows. At (A) the launching rocket lifts the vehicle from earth in the initial boost phase—when the first rocket stage has burnt out it falls away and the remaining stage coasts along an elliptical path (B) to the maximum altitude of the ellipse (C). If no more power were applied at this point the payload would fall to earth like a ballistic rocket, but the second stage rocket then comes into action and gives the necessary increase in velocity to establish the satellite in its orbit. As it burns out, the second stage falls away and the satellite is released into its free orbit. In some cases more than one stage is used in each of these phases.

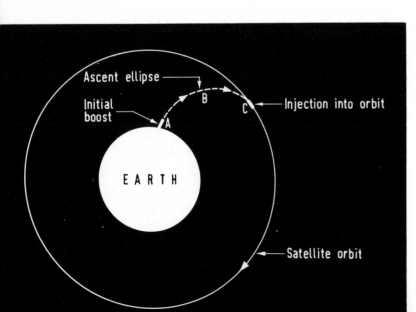

Ascent ellipse

Initial boost

B

C — Injection into orbit

EARTH

Satellite orbit

42

propulsion are constantly under study, and the use of nuclear fuels to replace the chemical fuels seems attractive. As one chemical element is transmuted into another, there is a release of nuclear energy. The substance releasing this is called a nuclear fuel, and contains a tremendous amount of energy. This can be generated rapidly, but must be controlled and directed to create the reaction thrust before it could be useful for propulsion. This might be done, for example, by feeding liquid hydrogen to a small vessel like the combustion chamber of the liquid fuelled rocket. The energy of the nuclear fuel would then be used to heat the hydrogen, which would be converted to gas and emerge under immense pressure. Such jets can be ejected at speeds of several miles per sec. A great deal of development is necessary, however, before these fuels can be introduced. No metal at present can withstand the high temperatures and pressures, and in manned flight there must also be protection from the radioactive radiations produced in the nuclear reaction.

Another interesting type of propulsion under development is known as ion propulsion. In this kind of rocket engine the atoms of one of the alkali metals (generally caesium) is ionised and the charged ions accelerated by an electric field to give very high velocity through a nozzle. Although the thrust available is high, a large amount of electrical energy is required to accelerate the ions. It may be that some future rockets will use the nuclear fuel to drive the electric power plant needed in these ion engines.

The basic mode of re-entry into the earth's atmosphere is illustrated here. A ballistic rocket launched at (X) will describe the elliptical path (A) under free flight and will enter the atmosphere and reach the earth (if suitably designed to avoid burn up) at (Y). A body from space, such as a returning deep space probe or a meteorite, will approach the earth along a more open (approximately hyperbolic) path as shown at (B). In the case of satellites there are two possibilities. If normal processes occur the height of the satellite will gradually decrease and it will eventually enter the dense layers of the atmosphere and burn up along a path such as (C). In controlled or manned re-entry a retro-rocket is fired at (Z) before the burn-up orbit is approached and the path to earth is along (D). The steepness of this re-entry path is determined by the aerodynamic characteristics of the vehicle and the power of the retro-rockets.

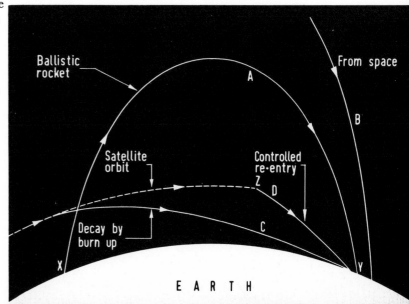

4 Some early results of the work with earth satellites

THE PROBLEM OF TRACKING

Some of the satellites are large enough to be seen by reflected sunlight when the observer on earth is in darkness, and the most accurate measurements of the orbits of earth satellites are made by specially designed cameras which record the track of the satellite against the background of the stars as it moves across the sky. However, for normal purposes it is customary to place a low-powered radio transmitter in the satellite so that it can be followed across the sky by a small radio telescope.

As well as having a small beacon transmitter, the satellite has to be equipped with a radio transmitter which can send back to earth all the measurements made by the scientific instruments in the satellite. This is done by modulating the transmitted signal by a code corresponding to the output of the information of the instruments in the satellite. The results are 'telemetered' back to earth.

In the case of satellites which move around the earth at distances of only a few hundred miles, there is not much difficulty in receiving the beacon and telemetered signals on earth with simple apparatus and small aerials or radio telescopes. However, the situation changes with space probes travelling a quarter of a million miles to the moon or beyond to the nearest of the planets. The signal strength decreases as the square of the distance; hence either much more powerful transmitters must be used in the probes, or the receiving apparatus on earth must be improved. Since weight is such a critical factor in the space probes the first alternative is impossible, and so very large aerial systems like the radio telescope at Jodrell Bank have become essential to detect the faint signals reaching earth from distant space probes.

THE DISCOVERY OF THE ZONES OF TRAPPED PARTICLES
AROUND THE EARTH

As we move out from the surface of the earth the density of the atmosphere rapidly decreases so that it becomes difficult to breathe on Mt Everest, and the cabin of a jet airliner has to be artificially pressurised at 30,000 ft. At ten times this height, in a region 60 miles above the surface, new phenomena appear. The attenuated atmosphere is ionised, that is, the normally neutral atoms of the atmosphere (mostly oxygen and nitrogen) have lost an electron, and space is populated with these electrons and the positive ions of the oxygen and nitrogen atoms. This condition of the outer atmosphere which extends from about 60 to

250 miles above the surface of the earth is known as the ionosphere and is marked at (*A*) in the diagram. The changing state of the ionosphere, and the variations in density of the electrons through it, is complex; but it is known to be largely under solar control. That is, the soft X-rays and the ultra-violet radiation from the sun are absorbed in this region and split up the atoms into the positive ions and electrons.

From the practical point of view the ionosphere is important because we rely on the fact that radio waves of certain wave-lengths are reflected from it to give us round-the-world radio communication. It is in this region also that the brilliant displays of the aurora polaris occur, and the meteor particles evaporate to produce the familiar shooting stars. Until 1959 we believed that the top regions of this ionosphere, at a height of 250–300 miles, represented the outer shell of the earth's immediate environment in space. Then van Allen, using apparatus in the American Explorer satellites, and Vernov in the Russian

The major properties of the earth's atmosphere. The air which we breathe at ground-level is a mixture consisting of about 21 per cent of oxygen and 79 per cent of nitrogen molecules (with small proportions of rarer gases). These proportions do not change very much with increasing height above the surface for the first 60 miles of ascent, although the density of the air at 60 miles is only $\frac{1}{10,000}$ of that at sea-level. Above 60 miles the oxygen molecules are dissociated by the radiation from the sun into atomic oxygen. In this region the solar ultra-violet X-rays are absorbed and this ejects an electron from the air atoms so that in this region marked (*A*) the atmosphere is ionised. The region of the atmosphere which protects us from the harmful solar radiations and the meteoric particles is this region marked (*A*) and below. Above 600 miles helium is the predominant constituent of the atmosphere, and above 1,500 miles, hydrogen, which merges into the inter-planetary medium. At 600 miles the density of the atmosphere is less than a million-millionth of the density at sea-level. At 1,500 miles it is less than a million million-millionth of that at sea-level.

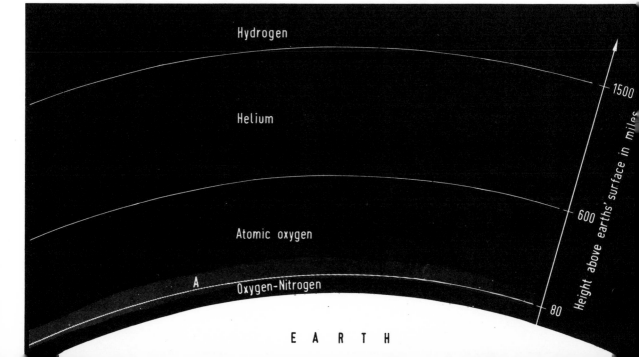

Hydrogen

Helium

Atomic oxygen

A   Oxygen-Nitrogen

1500

600

80

Height above earths' surface in miles

E A R T H

[*Opposite*] The density of the upper atmosphere decreases as shown in the diagram on page 45, and at an altitude of about 6,000 miles the density merges into that of the interplanetary hydrogen gas. This was believed to be the boundary region of the atmosphere until the discovery of the zones of particles trapped in the earth's magnetic field. The particles are electrons and protons, extending from about an earth radius (4,000 miles) above the surface of the earth to over 50,000 miles into space. This entire region is full of electrons or protons of various energies and at differing concentrations. The situation is variable and seems to depend on solar conditions—at least in the outer regions, but there is evidence of a concentration of protons in an inner zone at (*B*), and of electrons in an outer zone at (*C*). The study of the nature and energy of the particles in these regions is an important part of the current investigations by earth satellites and space probes.

Sputniks, made the remarkable discovery that out to distances of many thousands of miles the earth was surrounded by extensive zones of particles. After several years of intensive investigation by instruments carried in earth satellites and space probes, our knowledge of these 'van Allen zones' remains fragmentary, but the following points are well established.

The particles in the zones are either protons (the positive nuclei of hydrogen atoms) or electrons, and they are 'trapped' in the magnetic field of the earth. The magnetic field lines of the earth move out into space from one hemisphere to the other as illustrated in the diagram at (*XY*). A charged particle, such as a proton or electron, injected into this region of space may be trapped and constrained to move between the two hemispheres. It does this by spiralling around the lines of force as indicated at (*S*), and when it reaches the 'mirror points' at (*M*) its motion is reversed. The movement between the two hemispheres will take only a second and the entire system of spiralling particles is rotating about once a day to form shells around the earth.

We know that vast numbers of protons and electrons are trapped in this way around the earth, and there is strong evidence that there may be two main regions shown at (*B*) and (*C*). The inner zone (*B*), closest to earth, seems to be rather stable and predominantly composed of protons, whereas the outer region at (*C*) may contain mostly electrons and is extremely variable in position and intensity. Recently evidence has been obtained that the concentrations at (*B*) and (*C*) are special manifestations of a continuum of particles filling the entire zone from a few hundred to 50,000 miles away from the earth. Where do these particles come from? No one knows. Probably the protons at (*B*) are the result of neutrons which are generated in the earth's atmosphere by cosmic ray bombardment. These move out into space and decay into protons and electrons which are trapped in the zones. The electrons in (*C*) are extremely sensitive to events on the sun. A big solar eruption may deplete this radiation belt after which it takes days to become repopulated. This led to the suggestion that electrons were coming from the solar corona as a 'solar wind', but there are now arguments against this view.

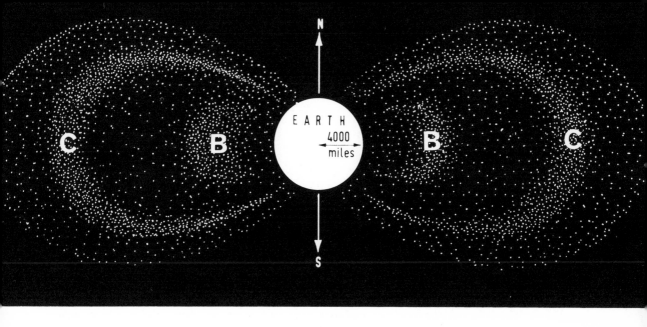

[*Below*]   The process by which charged particles are trapped in the earth's magnetic field is shown here. The magnetic lines of force of the earth moves out into space from the northern to the southern hemisphere as shown at (*XY*). If a charged particle is injected into these regions it will spiral around a line of force as at (*S*) and will make the traverse between the two hemispheres in about a second. At the 'mirror points' (*M*) the motion of the particle will be reversed and it will continue to spiral between the north and south hemispheres until it finally collides with a particle of the atmosphere and loses its energy. In addition to the motion between the north and south hemispheres, the orbits drift around the earth (the electrons or negatively charged particles in the westward direction and the protons or positively charged particles in the eastward direction). Thus about a day after injection, such charged particles will form a shell around the earth (sometimes likened to the scales of an onion). The protons and electrons are injected into the trapping regions naturally, either by the decay of particles moving out from the atmosphere or by particles reaching the vicinity of the earth after being ejected by the sun. Artificial injection can also be made—for example, by the radioactive decay products resulting from the explosion of a nuclear bomb in the region.

It is only beyond these zones, 50,000 miles from the earth, that the regions of outer space begin, not, as hitherto believed, at 250–300 miles from its surface, just beyond the ionosphere. Beyond the van Allen zones the solar wind, consisting of streams of electrons continuously blown out from the solar atmosphere (acquiring particular intensity during solar eruptions) reaches a compromise with the earth's own geophysical environment. Scientists are beginning to visualise the earth and planets as bodies enveloped in the sun's atmosphere, closely under solar control in the environmental as well as the gravitational sense.

In 1958, and again in 1962, the American military authorities exploded a nuclear bomb at a height of a few hundred miles above the earth. The electrons which resulted from the radioactive disintegrations of the particles in the bomb were trapped in the earth's magnetic field, and formed new radiation zones. Thus the 1958 and 1962 explosions gave rise to a zone of electrons concentrated between the inner and outer van Allen zones, and in addition the 1962 explosion set up another zone at an altitude lower than that of the zone of natural particles. Because the electrons in this new zone penetrate the upper reaches of the atmosphere at the mirror points, it is decaying rapidly, but the zone at the higher altitude will last for many years.

There is a sharp division of opinion as to whether these tests, which are carried out primarily for military reasons, constitute the best way to investigate the scientific features of the natural zones, or whether they will cause such confusion that correct scientific investigation will become impossible.

THE METEORS AND MICROMETEORITES

As well as the magnetic trapping of ionised particles in the radiation belts, there is also a gravitational trapping of fine dust in the vicinity of the earth. From recent analysis of micrometeorite recordings in the American satellites, Dr Whipple of Harvard has suggested that a large quantity of this dust is travelling round the earth, trapped in the earth's gravitational field. The dust must be part of the concentration of meteors, or shooting stars, which enter the earth's atmosphere in great numbers. In its journey through space the earth encounters a vast debris of small particles chiefly composed of stone or iron. Occasionally they are so large that they penetrate the earth's atmosphere and fall as meteorites. In ancient times when such an event took place and destroyed a city, it was believed to be an act of vengeance sent from heaven for the punishment of Man's wickedness. The Siberian meteorite of 1908 felled forests for 20 sq. miles and was followed in 1947 by another large one. The crater in Arizona, ¾ mile across and 500 ft. deep, was made by a meteorite in prehistoric times which must have weighed 1 million tons.

Meteors are observed when the small particles are heated by friction on entering the outer layers of the atmosphere, and evaporate about 60 miles above its surface, leaving a transient trail of light. Ten or more per hour can be seen on any clear night, and at certain times of the year huge showers of them are observed, but almost all are exploded into harmless dust by the shielding atmosphere. The daily count of these tiny grains of dust is over 8,000 million, and they weigh only about 1/10,000 gramme. Smaller sizes may be detected by radio techniques, and their numbers increase by about $2\frac{1}{2}$ times for every fainter magnitude, endlessly as the size decreases, so that probably a million million are being swept up by the earth every day. When the size of the particle is less than a millimetre it is too small to burn up, for then the ratio of surface area to mass is so large that the energy of interaction is radiated away on entering the atmosphere, and the flight of the dust grain is stopped before evaporation occurs. These micrometeorites then fall to the earth as dust. By studying deposits on the ocean bed it is estimated that the earth collects about a million tons a year in this way. This estimate has been confirmed by collecting the micrometeorites on special plates placed in a dust-free atmosphere or on a mountain-top, for example.

Many of the American and Russian satellites have been equipped with some form of detector to measure the impact of these micrometeorites before they enter the atmosphere. The early techniques used have now been refined to greater accuracy. Originally the micrometeorites were allowed to collide with a diaphragm equipped with a microphone, so that the sound of the dust grain hitting the diaphragm was telemetered back to earth. In practice, however, the microphone recorded other noises as well and the calibration also was uncertain. Improved techniques indicate that for particles weighing a hundred millionth of a gramme the rate of impact is one particle per 1,000 seconds over an area of 1 sq. in. For particles weighing a thousand millionth of a gramme the rate is 1 every 100 seconds. The quantity of the dust is 1,000–10,000 times greater than that of the particles large enough to burn up in the atmosphere.

These two fields of work arising out of the early observations with satellites have increased Man's knowledge of the area immediately surrounding the earth, and pushed back the frontiers of outer space to a distance of more than 50,000 miles. Within that range he has discovered the presence of the trapped protons and electrons in the van Allen zones, and has attained much more knowledge of the very fine dust in the vicinity of the earth.

Many other results have already been achieved by the use of earth satellites. For example, merely by observing the changes in the orbits of the satellites more accurate measurements have been made of the degree to which the earth is flattened at the poles. Departures from perfect sphericity produce irregularities in the movements of the satellites. From this work it may become apparent whether the earth's a-sphericity is reflected in its shape or in some uneven

[*continued on page* 54]

49

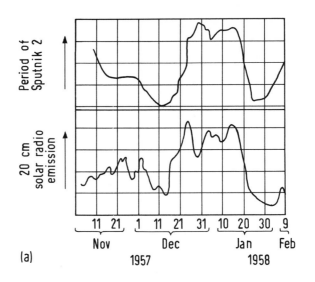

(a)

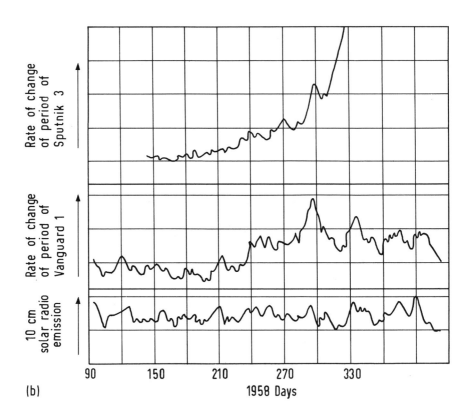

(b)

[*Opposite*]   The development of scientific ideas through spontaneous international collaboration is well illustrated by the diagram. Luigi Jacchia of the Harvard Observatory in America was interested in the precise orbits of earth satellites. From the accurate camera measurements on the orbit of the Russian Sputnik II, Jacchia discovered that from day to day there were large and apparently random fluctuations in the atmospheric drag acting on the satellite. His report on this came to the notice of Dr Priester in Germany, who thought that the variations might be produced by radiation emitted from the vicinity of sun-spots. The radio waves from the sun on wave-lengths of 20 cm. are known to be a close indication of the general level of solar activity and Priester found the close correlation shown in (*a*) between these events and the drag on Sputnik II. On hearing of these results, Jacchia then placed his drag curves for Sputnik III and Vanguard I against the 10-cm. solar radio emissions from the sun and found the excellent correlation shown in (*b*). The interpretation of this is as follows: the extreme ultra-violet radiation from the sun is absorbed in the region of the atmosphere from 90 to 150 miles altitude. During the intense periods of solar activity the amount of energy absorbed is sufficient to heat the atmosphere in this region. This causes an expansion upward and a large increase in the density of the highly attenuated atmosphere with a consequently prominent effect on the drag of the satellite.

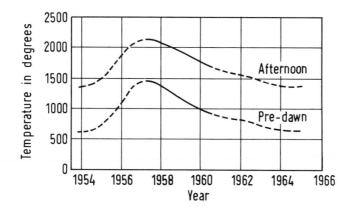

[*Above*]   The remarkable manner in which the relations shown in the diagrams (*a*) and (*b*) may be used to predict the future variations of the solar influence on the upper atmosphere is shown here. The unbroken lines give Priester's results, showing the change in the upper atmospheric temperature since the start of the satellite drag measurements in 1957. As shown in the earlier diagrams, this is closely correlated with the 20-cm. radio emissions from the sun. The variation of this solar activity throughout the eleven-year solar cycle is well known, and here Priester has estimated, as shown by the broken lines, the past variations in the upper atmospheric temperature back to 1954 and predicted the future variations to 1965. This kind of prediction might become significant for long-term weather forecasting if the relation between changes in the upper atmospheric temperatures and conditions in the lower regions of the atmosphere can be discovered.

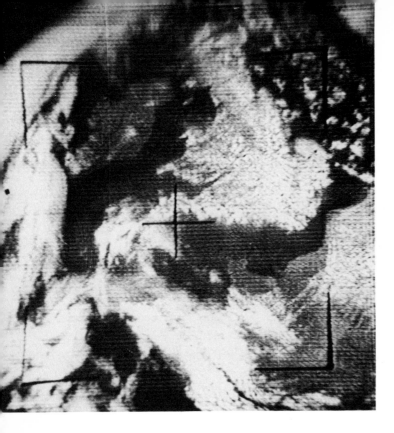

One of the most remarkable applications of earth satellites, which is potentially of great importance to human beings, is the ability to study the earth's surface and its cloud cover from above. An immediate application has been the identification of cyclones in the early stages of their formation. The new possibilities for the almost simultaneous and frequent interpretation of cloud structures all over the earth may well revolutionise the science of meteorology, particularly in respect of the improvement of long-range weather forecasts, and the studies of the possibility of gaining some measure of control over the

[*continued opposite*]

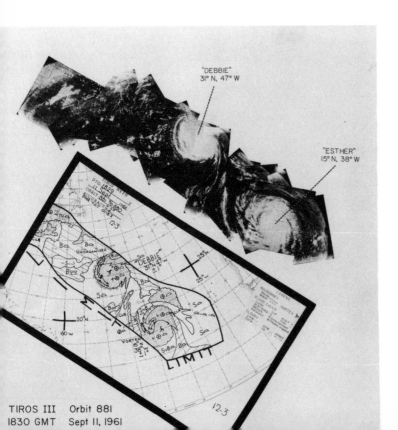

TIROS III   Orbit 881
1830 GMT   Sept 11, 1961

"DEBBIE"
31° N, 47° W

"ESTHER"
15° N, 38° W

[*Below, left*]   The cameras in the Tiros satellites may either be commanded from the ground to take pictures or may be 'programmed' to take pictures automatically of parts of the earth when Tiros is out of range of the ground command station. These are transmitted to earth by scanning the film and using the equivalent of a television technique to impress the details of the picture on the telemetery. At the ground station the signals are fed on to a television tube, where a camera photographs each television picture. It takes about 15 minutes to develop and print a positive film from one such interrogation of Tiros, suitable to be handed to a meteorologist. This illustration is a mosaic of a series of pictures from Tiros III on 11 September 1961 showing the hurricanes 'Debbie' and 'Esther'.

52

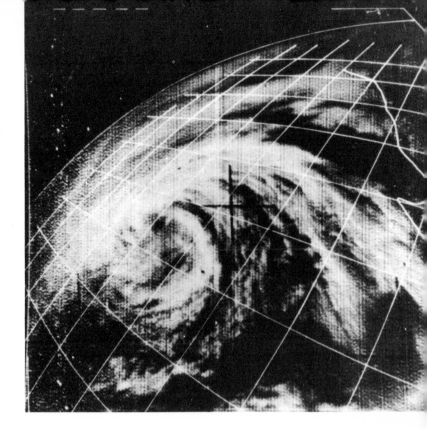

[continued] climate. All the investigations so far have been carried out with the United States Tiros satellites. These satellites, which weigh less than 300 lb., have been placed in orbit 300 to 600 miles above the earth. Tiros I was launched on 1 April 1960; Tiros II on 23 November 1960; Tiros III on 12 July 1961. The latest in the series, Tiros VI, was launched on 18 September 1962. This photograph shows a remarkable picture of the British Isles and northern Europe photographed by Tiros IV on its 919th orbit at 1328 G.M.T. on 13 April 1962. Ireland and a good deal of northern Europe is free of cloud, but England, Wales and Scotland are covered with broken cloud.

[Above]   A Tiros photograph of the tropical storm 'Liza' over the eastern Pacific at 1835 G.M.T. on 19 July 1961. The spiral cloud formation is seen to extend several hundred miles from the cloud centre.

[Right]   The typhoon 'Ruth' photographed by Tiros V on its 855th orbit in August 1962. The centre of the typhoon which was in the Pacific, north-east of Hawaii, could be located accurately from this photograph.

53

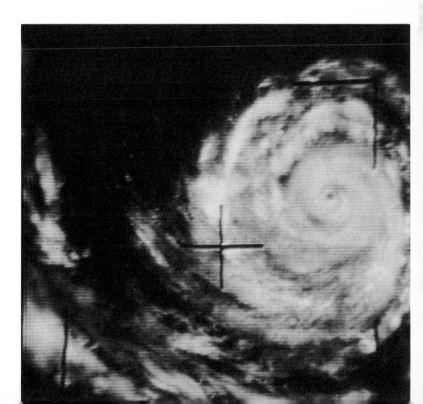

distribution of dense material in its interior. Also from a study of the small variation in the orbits by analysing the photographic trails of the satellites, there has been an important accumulation of knowledge about the variation in density of the atmosphere with height, and of the presence of fluctuations at heights of more than 100 miles which were not previously suspected.

In the next chapter, as instruments are carried even farther from the earth by space probes, studies of the more distant parts of the solar system will be described.

ROCKETS TO THE MOON

As more powerful rockets were built, so instruments could be carried in capsules escaping farther and farther from the earth. The first known attempt of Man to launch a rocket deep into space was the initial American one in the Pioneer series which unfortunately blew up 80 seconds after launching in August 1958. This was followed in October of that year by Pioneer I. Although it was intended to reach the moon it did not have sufficient velocity to do so and fell back into the earth's atmosphere after travelling over 70,000 miles into space. Pioneer I failed in its primary purpose, but collected much valuable information, particularly about the outer van Allen zone. Lunik I, launched by the Russians in January 1959, travelled past the moon and eventually entered an orbit around the sun with a period of 450 days, but Lunik II, launched in September of the same year, continued on course after the most accurate launch achieved up to this time, and on 13 September the high-pitched whistling sounds, to which scientists tracking with the Jodrell Bank telescope had been listening for hours, suddenly ceased, and the second Soviet space rocket reached the surface of the moon. On a journey of 235,497 miles it was 83 seconds later than the predicted impact time. The capsule came down in the area of Mare Tranquillitatis, Mare Serenitatis and Mare Vaporum. Its speed of impact was 2·05 miles per sec., and as it hit the moon the radio containers holding scientific and measuring equipment ceased to function. Among the instruments carried in the capsule were some to measure the intensity of the zones of radiation surrounding the earth, described in the previous chapter, and others to study the composition of the matter of which meteoric particles and interplanetary gas are formed.

This time there was a final stage rocket weighing 324 lb. without fuel, which separated at a predetermined time, and after separation the capsule and the last stage of the rocket travelled along slightly different paths. On this final stage of the journey a radio circuit was switched on in the capsule to act as a 'moon altimeter'. Photographs were obtained by Russian observers and French astronomers at the St Michel de Provence Observatory of the artificial comet emitted by the rocket in the form of a sodium cloud. This helped the Russians to determine the rocket's trajectory more accurately than by the radio tracking of its beacon.

All necessary steps were taken to ensure that no earthly micro-organisms were carried by the rocket which might contaminate the moon, and prevent

[*continued on page* 57]

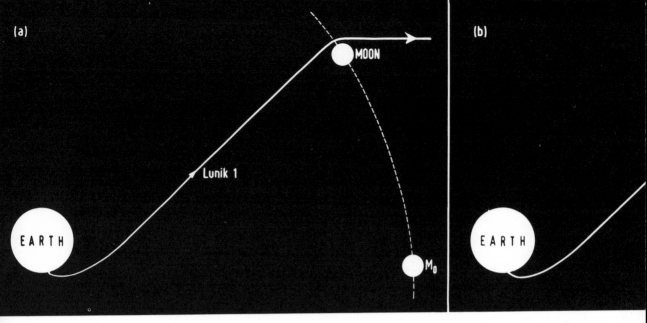

(a)   (b)

[*Above*]   The critical conditions which apply to the launching of a rocket to the moon are indicated in this diagram showing the orbits of the three Russian Luniks. The minimum velocity which will cause a vehicle to reach the moon is only slightly less than the escape velocity from earth of 36,700 ft. per sec. (or 35,400 ft., if the vehicle is injected into its orbit 300 miles above the earth, which is a more usual practical situation). For a given direction of launch, small errors of as little as 50–100 ft. per sec. in this initial velocity will cause the vehicle to miss the moon entirely. This happened to Lunik I, which went close enough to the moon to be deflected by its gravitational field (*a*), and the Lunik then entered an orbit around the sun. The accuracy of the Lunik II launching was good enough to bring it closer to the moon so that it eventually fell to the lunar surface under the gravitational pull of the moon (*b*). The speed of launching for Lunik III was intentionally fixed below the escape velocity so that it entered an elliptical orbit which just encompassed the moon at its apogee (*c*). In other words, Lunik III was launched as an earth satellite and after passing near the moon entered an earth satellite orbit with a period of about 7 days. When it reached the apogee of its orbit the second time (*P*) the moon had, of course, travelled on to (M_1). In each diagram the broken curve represents the motion of the moon around the earth; and the position of the moon relative to earth at the moment of launching is shown at (M_0).

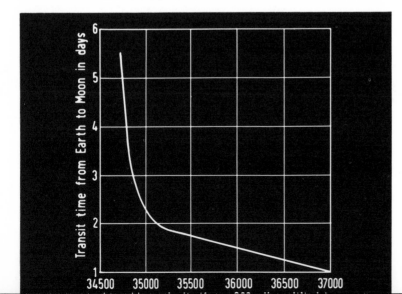

[*Left*]   The transit time of a vehicle fr[om] the earth to the moon depends critically [on] the launching velocity as shown in t[he] graph which gives the time in days as a function of the initial velocity from a point 300 miles above the earth's surfa[ce]. This corresponds to a reasonable practi[cal] case. The escape velocity is then 35,400 ft. per sec. (corresponding to 36,700 ft. p[er] sec. from the surface of the earth). Luni[k] II took about $1\frac{1}{2}$ days over the journey from the earth to the moon and its initi[al]

56

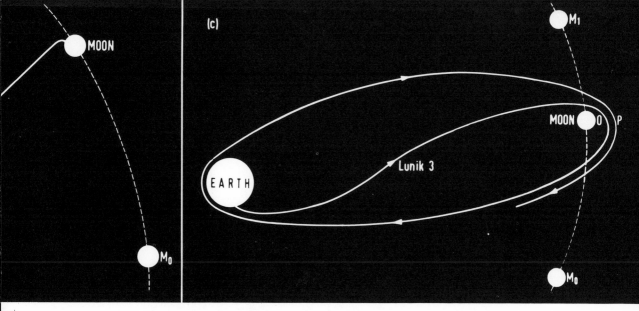

future study of the material existing there. In October 1959 the next important
stage was reached when a Russian moon rocket, Lunik III, was launched on
a course which carried it once round behind the moon and then back towards
the earth. Inside the vehicle was equipment for photographing the far side of
the moon, and this was successfully operated so that pictures of the 40 per cent
of the moon's surface never before observed by Man were obtained. (The moon

[*continued on page* 59]

[*Below, right*]   If a vehicle is to be fired from earth and placed in a satellite orbit
around the moon, then it must be decelerated by firing retro-rockets near the point
of closest approach of the vehicle to the moon as indicated in this diagram. The
velocity which a vehicle has in the vicinity of the moon as a result of the launching
from earth is too great to allow it to be captured in a satellite orbit around the
moon. It will either hit the moon (as with Lunik II) or be deflected and pass on
(as with Luniks I and III). Even with the minimum launching velocity from earth,
the speed of the vehicle near the moon is 8,000 ft. per sec., and retro-rockets must
be fired to reduce this to about 4,000 ft. per sec. if the vehicle is to go into a lunar
orbit. This feat has not yet been accomplished—although it had been hoped to
do this with the original American Pioneer moon probes.

ocity was therefore in the neighbour-
od of 35,600 ft. per sec. On the other
nd, the American Pioneer and Ranger
on rockets had planned transit times
2·6 days, corresponding to a launching
ocity of about 34,900 ft. per sec. Only
ut 2½ per cent change in the initial
ocity gives this big difference in transit
e. The longest time of 5½ days
responds to the minimum launching
ocity which will cause the vehicle to
ch the moon.

57

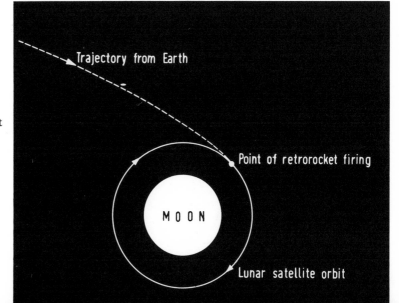

[*Opposite* (*a*) *and above* (*b*)] Lunik III, the historic Russian moon probe launched on
4 October 1959, which photographed the hidden side of the moon. The camera lens
can be seen clearly in (*a*). There were two photographic systems with lenses of
different focal lengths to obtain close-ups and photographs of the whole disk. The
photography was on 35-mm. film which was processed in the probe. The film was
then scanned and the images transmitted back to earth by a television scanning
technique. Illustration (*b*) is a reconstruction of the relative positions of the moon
and the Lunik when the photographs were taken. The arrows show the direction
of the sun's rays. The photography was carried out on command by a signal
transmitted from earth. It began at 06^h 30^m Moscow time on 7 October when the
Lunik was 41,000 miles from the moon and continued until 07^h 10^m Moscow time
when the Lunik was 42,800 miles from the moon.

always turns the same face towards earth as it rotates once on its axis during
the 28 days in which it revolves round the earth.) The direction and velocity of
launching of this rocket were most critical matters, since it had to be placed in
an orbit which effectively made it an earth satellite, but with a major axis so
large that at apogee it just passed around the moon.

This wholly successful attempt still provides the only photographic records of
the 'dark' side of the moon which Man possesses (1962), and together these first
moon shots, American and Russian, made large contributions to his knowledge

[*continued on page* 62]

59

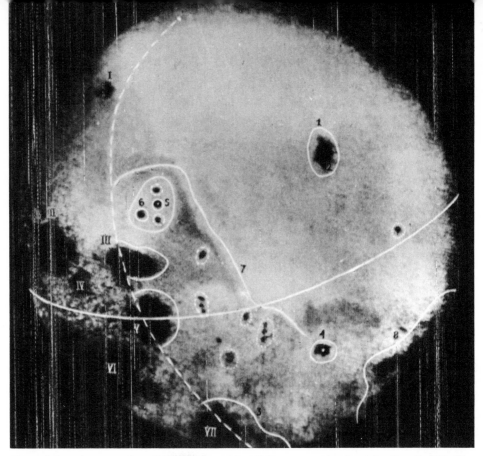

One of the photographs of the reverse side of the moon obtained by Lunik III. The definition is relatively poor compared with the normal lunar photographs taken from earth, but even so, it is evident that the far side of the moon contains fewer 'seas' and contrasting areas than the forward side seen from earth. The solid line across the moon is the lunar equator and the dotted line is the border between the part of the moon which can be seen from earth (to the left) and the unseen part. The objects marked with Roman numerals are those which can be seen from earth, as follows:

I = Humboldt Sea
II = Sea of Crisis
III = Regional Sea
IV = Sea of Waves
V = Smyth's Sea
VI = Sea of Fertility
VII = South Sea

The Russians named the features on the hidden side which are numbered with Arabic numerals as follows:

1 = a 200-mile crater—the Moscow Sea
2 = the Astronauts Bay of the Moscow Sea
3 = continuation of the South Sea on the moon's reverse side
4 = crater of main Tsiolkovsky hill
5 = crater of central Lomonosov hill
6 = Joliot Curie crater
7 = Sovietsky mountain range
8 = Dream Sea

60

The north-east quadrant of the moon photographed by the 100-in. telescope on Mt Wilson, in which the Mare Imbrium (Sea of Rains) is predominant. The crater in the bottom left of the photograph is Copernicus. The smaller crater to the north-west of this is Eratosthenes. In the group of three craters near the centre right Archimedes is the largest, followed by Aristillus and Autolycus. The large crater to the north of this group is Plato. Mare Frigoris (the Sea of Gold) is to the north of Plato. The mountain ranges near Copernicus are the Carpathians and the Appenines begin under the crater of Eratosthenes. The Alps extend south-east from the crater Plato, and are the size of Switzerland. The largest craters are the size of a big English county, and the smallest visible on this photograph would contain a large town. The highest mountain on the moon (not on this photograph) is as high as Mt Everest. The 'Maria' or 'Seas' were named when the dark areas were believed to be water. They are, in fact, plains of ash and dust. There is no water on the moon, unless some is trapped in small quantities as ice below the surface or in crevices shielded from the sun. Contrary to earlier beliefs, the mountain slopes are not thought to be precipitous and recent work indicates that slopes are almost everywhere less than $10°$—probably because the outlines are rounded off by thick dust.

61

of the radiation zones, through which the rockets passed; all this valuable information was received during flight from transmitters powered by solar batteries.

It is remarkable that since the exploits of Luniks II and III in September and October 1959 there have been no further successful lunar probes. In fact, there has been no announcement of a Russian attempt, although, since their failures are never known for certain, it is possible that they have made unsuccessful attempts.[1] On the other hand, the Americans have tried repeatedly with little success. Four other attempts were made in the Pioneer series in 1958 to 1960. Pioneer IV, launched on 3 March 1959, missed the moon and like Lunik I went into a solar orbit. Pioneer III, launched on 6 December 1958, stayed up for only a day, like Pioneer I; and Pioneer VI, which was to have been launched in the autumn of 1960 as a lunar probe, blew up during the launching process.

The Ranger series of lunar probes of 1961 and 1962 have not been much more successful. Rangers I and II, launched on 23 August and 18 November 1961 respectively, were deep space tests of the new system which were partially successful. Rangers III, IV and V were intended to hit the moon and in doing so to 'rough land' a small instrument package which would continue to transmit seismic information to the earth. On 26 January 1962 Ranger III was not launched with sufficient accuracy to hit the moon and went into an orbit around the sun with a period of 406 days. Like many other lunar probe failures, it gave valuable information about the conditions in interplanetary space. Ranger IV launched on 23 April 1962 developed trouble with its radio apparatus and could not be commanded from earth. It is believed to have crash landed on the reverse side of the moon on 26 April. Ranger V launched on 18 October 1962 passed within 300 miles of the moon on 21 October, but its solar cells did not charge the batteries, which ran down a few hours after launching.

A leader writer in *New York Times* on 5 October 1959 says, with magnanimity:

> The sheer growth of mankind's—particularly Soviet—capabilities in this field staggers the imagination. Already it is clear that the Nineteen Sixties will see man explore the solar system and perhaps even land on the moon.

The era of great scientific advance was coinciding with a period of tremendous technical rivalry between East and West and the work of the inquiring scientists was henceforth to tangle with the work of those concerned with the conflict in space.

The new science of astronautics needed the very closest co-operation between scientist and engineer. Equipment was required which would function perfectly

[1] Lunik IV was launched by the Russians on 2 April 1963. This was widely believed to be an attempt to land instruments on the moon, but it missed its target, and the closest approach to the moon was 5,000 miles on 5 April.

over very long periods with virtually no attention. This demanded the most rigorous testing and everything had to be designed with excessive care, based on a knowledge of space environments provided by the scientist to the engineer. The vehicles were to carry first instruments, then animals and then the scientist himself, which would raise the problem of maintaining life away from the earth's surface. There was also the possibility that he might encounter life in some form in other parts of the universe, in fact the view of his place in the general scheme of things was going to be extended in a similar way to the revolution in thinking which followed the invention of the telescope. Space exploration would require international co-operation on a large scale to be effective, for just as astronomers have always assisted one another in different parts of the globe to observe celestial bodies, so the study of artificial celestial bodies demands even closer co-operation. Their launching, retrieval and in many cases the short-lived opportunities they provide for study, as well as agreement on frequency allocations, make this essential.

The practical uses soon to be demonstrated by the creation of these space vehicles will be described later, for the late fifties and early sixties proved to be a period of 'firsts', with more possibilities being glimpsed every few months as newspapers announced an American or Russian success.

THE APPROACH TO THE PLANETS

Of the lunar probes so far mentioned four—Lunik I, Pioneer IV, Ranger III and Ranger V—missed their target and continued past the moon into helio-centric orbits around the sun, with periods of 450 days (Lunik I), 398 days (Pioneer IV), 406 days (Ranger III) and 370 days (Ranger V). However, their power supply systems were designed for a lunar journey of a few days and they could be tracked only to about 400,000 miles before contact was lost.

The first successful penetration deep into space was achieved by the American probe Pioneer V, launched on 11 March 1960. It was originally intended to send this probe towards the planet Venus, but because of delays it was eventually launched as a deep space probe without any specific planetary targets. Pioneer V was a great success. Its transmitters could be switched on and off by a signal sent out from the telescope at Jodrell Bank. It was commanded in this manner every day until the end of June when it was 23 million miles from earth. At that distance the radio command signal took 2 minutes to travel from the telescope to the probe, thus after pressing the command button at Jodrell Bank it was 4 minutes before the signals came back from Pioneer V. Unfortunately the batteries, which were being charged by the solar energy collected by cells mounted on four paddle-wheels, developed some kind of leak and contact was lost at that distance. A vast amount of important scientific data was collected, particularly about the magnetic fields and cosmic rays in interplanetary space. For example, Pioneer V gave the first real experimental information indicating

63

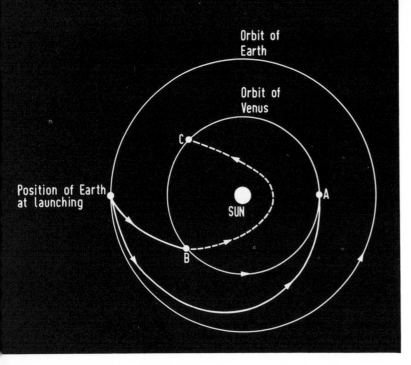

Orbit of
Earth

Orbit of
Venus

C

SUN

A

B

Position of Earth
at launching

As explained in Chapter 3, in order to reach the vicinity of a planet a vehicle must be fired from earth with a velocity exceeding the escape velocity of 36,700 ft. per sec. so that it enters an elliptical orbit around the sun. A number of trajectories are possible, but only one for minimum energy and hence maximum payload. This case occurs when the vehicle traverses one half of the ellipse between the perihelion and aphelion points of the orbit around the sun. This is illustrated in the diagram for the case of Venus. In the optimum case the launching from earth must be made so that the vehicle reaches the planet when it is at (A)—involving a transit time of 4 months. The transit time to meet the planet at (B) would be less, but the launching would have to be made with greater initial velocity—and hence with less payload for a given rocket. For an encounter at (C) both transit time and initial velocity would be greater than for case (A). With the rocket power at present available it is not possible to depart significantly from the optimum case (A). In fact, if the most favourable launch date were exceeded by 2 months then the initial velocity would have to be about 44,000 ft. per sec. The most favourable launch dates in the future are as follows:

Mars	*Venus*	*Jupiter*
23 December 1964	28 March 1964	June 1965
26 January 1967	27 October 1965	September 1966
28 February 1969	5 June 1967	November 1967
February/March 1971	11 January 1969	January/February 1969
	August 1970	April 1970
		June/July 1971

that there are travelling magnetic fields in space, associated with the streams of particles shot out by the sun during solar eruptions. Pioneer V is now a silent object orbiting the sun as an artificial planet every 311 days.

The next great excitement in deep space investigation came on 12 February 1961 when the Russians announced that they had launched a probe towards the planet Venus. This announcement was memorable because the launching used a new technique whereby a heavy satellite is placed in a sputnik-like orbit around the earth, and then after a period of about half an hour the probe is launched from this space platform. This technique has become commonplace for deep space launchings, because the use of the 'parking orbit', as it is called by the Americans, enables the maximum advantage to be obtained of the earth's own orbital velocity. Unfortunately the signals from this Venus probe ceased

The photograph of Venus reveals nothing but a thick cloud layer, and the only certain content of its atmosphere is a large concentration of carbon dioxide. Photographic and visual observations fail to reveal how fast the planet is rotating, but it seems certain that this will soon be determined from the radar observations of the planet. The first man-made object to approach close to the planet was the American space probe Mariner II, which passed 22,000 miles from it on 14 December 1962. It can be assumed with confidence that Mariner II and its successors will soon give us the vital information about the nature of the planet's surface which is obscured from view by the cloud cover.

after about a week for reasons which are not fully understood. In June two Russian scientists came to Jodrell Bank for a final attempt to find signals from the probe—a striking illustration of the international co-operation which takes place in scientific research. This Venus probe, like Pioneer V, is now a silent artificial planet of the sun travelling around it every 300 days.

The next favourable opportunity for launching probes to Venus occurred during the summer of 1962, and both Russia and America were expected to renew their attempts. The Americans tried twice, once with Mariner I, which failed, and then again on 27 August with Mariner II, which was successful. According to American sources the Russians tried, but failed, although this has not been acknowledged by the Russians.

Mariner II, like Pioneer V, was a highly successful venture. It weighed 447 lb., and the solar panels contained 9,800 solar cells extending over 27 sq. ft. in area. These converted the sun's energy into 148 to 222 watts of power to charge the batteries. Mariner contained six experiments. Four of these gave information about the magnetic fields, ionised particles and dust particles, as the probe travelled through space, and the other two were designed to operate when Mariner was close to Venus so that information about the condition of the atmosphere and surface of the planet could be obtained. This planet, although one of our closest neighbours in space, is so thickly covered with cloud that we do not know how fast it is rotating or whether its surface is an arid desert or an ocean. One experiment carried a radiometer in order to measure the strength of the radiation from the planet at wave-lengths of 13·5 and 19 mm.

[*continued on page* 67]

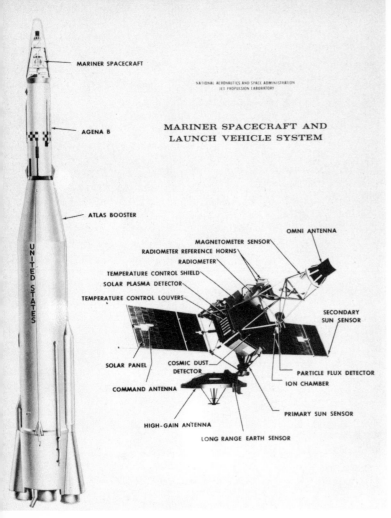

NATIONAL AERONAUTICS AND SPACE ADMINISTRATION
JET PROPULSION LABORATORY

MARINER SPACECRAFT
MARINER SPACECRAFT AND
LAUNCH VEHICLE SYSTEM

AGENA B

ATLAS BOOSTER

UNITED STATES

MAGNETOMETER SENSOR
OMNI ANTENNA
RADIOMETER REFERENCE HORNS
RADIOMETER
TEMPERATURE CONTROL SHIELD
SOLAR PLASMA DETECTOR
TEMPERATURE CONTROL LOUVERS

SECONDARY
SUN SENSOR

SOLAR PANEL
COSMIC DUST DETECTOR
PARTICLE FLUX DETECTOR
ION CHAMBER
COMMAND ANTENNA

PRIMARY SUN SENSOR
HIGH-GAIN ANTENNA
LONG RANGE EARTH SENSOR

Drawings of Mariner II and its launching rocket. The probe was launched from Cape Canaveral on 27 August 1962 and passed 22,000 miles from Venus on 14 December 1962 after a journey of 180 million miles in space. The distance of the probe from earth at the close approach to the planet was 35 million miles. The earth and sun sensors were installed for the automatic alignment of the probe so that the high-gain antenna, through which the telemetery was transmitted, was pointing accurately in the direction of the earth. The small command antenna is the aerial which received the command signals from the transmitter on earth. The experiments working during the interplanetary journey are marked solar plasma detector, cosmic dust detector, ion chamber, particle flux detector, and magnetometer sensor. The radiometer and radiometer reference horns refer to the two experiments in the millimetre and infra-red bands which operated in the vicinity of the planet.

At 13·5 mm. there is a water vapour absorption band, and if there is water vapour in the planet's atmosphere it will show up on this wave-length. At 19 mm. the radiometer was able to 'see' right through the atmosphere to the surface of the planet.

The other experiments measured the infra-red radiation and worked on a wave-length of 8 to 9, and 10 to 10·8 microns (a micron is one thousandth of a millimetre). When the planet is studied from earth on these wave-lengths the indicated temperature is below zero, but it is not clear whether this is a measurement of the cloud tops or of the surface. If the markings which can be seen on Venus are cloud breaks, then the 8 to 9 micron radiation will be from the surface, since the atmosphere is transparent in this range. On the other hand, the 10 to 10·8 micron radiation will come from the carbon dioxide which is known to be abundant in the planet's atmosphere. In fact, the preliminary results so far announced about the data collected by Mariner indicate that it measured the temperature of the surface of the planet and that this was very high—several hundred degrees centigrade.

In order that these two important experiments should work, it was necessary for Mariner to pass within a few thousand miles of Venus. For this high degree of accuracy to be achieved Mariner had to be sent on its journey with reserve rocket power on board so that slight adjustments could be made to its orbit. This 'midcourse correction' was successfully accomplished on 4 September 1962 when Mariner was 1½ million miles from earth, and it passed within 22,000 miles of Venus in mid December 1962. Mariner is now a silent object in orbit around the sun with a period of 348 days.

Jodrell Bank has been the scene of much international co-operation during the last few years. In June 1961 Professor Alla Massevich, Professor of Astrophysics in the University of Moscow, came to Jodrell Bank with Dr Khodarev who designed the equipment in the Russian Venus rocket, in order to search for signals from it. The two Russian scientists are seen here in the laboratory used for space operations immediately above the control room of the telescope. Dr J. G. Davies is on the left of the photograph and Professor Lovell is on the left of Professor Massevich.

On 1 November 1962 the Russians launched a probe designed to travel to the vicinity of the planet Mars. This probe—designated Mars I—probably reached the neighbourhood of the planet in May or early June 1963 (seven months after launching). According to Russian statements the initial trajectory was such that it should pass within a distance of 31,000 miles from the planet, but it was intended to correct the course so that when it reached the neighbourhood of the planet it would approach to a distance of between 600 and 6,000 miles. The payload weighed 2,000 lb., and in addition to the apparatus for investigating interplanetary space during the journey, it was intended to photograph the planet at close approach and transmit the photographs back to earth. Early in 1963 the payload developed a fault, contact was lost, so that these major objectives were not attained.

[*Below*]   The appearance of the planet Mars as photographed by the 200-in. telescope. Even the world's largest telescope fails to reveal any clear indications of the nature of the planetary surface. The main trouble is that even under the best conditions the turbulence of our own atmosphere blurs the finer details, and consequently there has been much discussion about the possible changes which can be observed on the planet. There seems general agreement that reddish-brown deserts make up one half of the surface and that there are polar caps, probably of hoar-frost, 5,000 miles across which diminish in size as the planet's summer approaches. The photograph with a blue filter (on the left) reveals the planet's tenuous atmosphere. The possible existence of some forms of organic development on Mars will probably remain a matter for speculation until space probes penetrate to the planet.

BLUE

BLUE

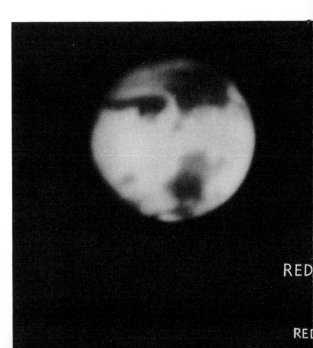

RED

RED

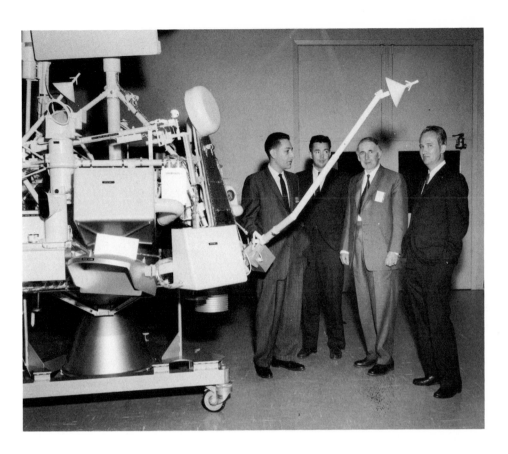

A full-scale mock-up of the Surveyor space craft which the United States hopes to land on the moon in 1964. Surveyor contains instruments for drilling into the lunar surface, for crushing and analysing the samples, and then transmitting the information back to earth. This photograph was taken in April 1962 and shows Professor Lovell (second from right) with officials of the Hughes Aircraft Co., who are the main contractors for the space craft.

6 Man in space

God sells knowledge for labour, honour for risk.
ARABIC SAYING

GAGARIN: FIRST MAN IN SPACE

Chapters 3, 4 and 5 described some of the ways in which Man has been successful in placing his instruments away from the terrestrial environment, so that the range of his investigations has been enormously increased, and some of the first results of these experiments have been indicated. The next stage was for Man himself to accompany this equipment, so that the possibilities for its use would be considerably extended, by the presence of an intelligent being able to control its workings as occasion arose.

In the U.S. and U.S.S.R. plans were made for step-by-step programmes which would culminate in orbiting a man around the earth, and in both countries the programme included many experimental flights with capsules carrying animals first. Each vehicle had a definite set of scientific problems to solve, telemetering back to earth the data its instruments collected, so that even in cases where re-entry devices failed to operate, the information was received nevertheless.

The Tass announcement from Moscow on 12 April 1961 that the $4\frac{1}{2}$-ton space ship Vostok, carrying Pilot Yuri Gagarin, had landed safely after a single orbit was the climax of a great co-operative effort by scientists and engineers. Before this first journey in space by a man could be attempted, the man himself had to be submitted to tests of a most rigorous nature, and even after months of enduring these, and proving himself able to withstand tremendous physical and mental strains, the uncertainty of what might await him in the actual flight remained. Experiments with animals had demonstrated that strains associated with noise, acceleration and deceleration, and the condition of weightlessness, could be overcome, but how would a man react in similar situations? Tests had to be devised which would simulate these conditions, for example, the acceleration load from 'rest' to 60 m.p.h. in $\frac{1}{10}$ sec. of rocket take-off was reproduced, and human reactions were carefully recorded.

Other tests involved spending an hour listening to a whine of roaring and screeching noise recorded on tape and amplified so that there was no possibility of blocking one's ears from its sound. Then perhaps there would be a period, of unknown duration, alone, in complete silence and sometimes darkness. There was thorough training in memorising instructions, in working out navigational courses, continuing to operate controls in very high temperatures, as well as centrifugal tests.

Of all these problems that of the reaction of the human body to the forms of acceleration involved in the lift-off and return to earth, and to weightlessness in orbit, was the greatest. It was known that forces on the human body of more than ten times the normal force of gravity on earth would have to be sustained for periods of minutes during the ascent phase of the rocket. There existed already a good deal of information, obtained during high-speed manœuvring in fast aircraft, of the effects on a pilot of high g forces for short periods, and during crash landings extremely high g forces had been survived—but the body had to sustain these for only fractions of a second. The broad effects which are believed to take place are indicated in the following table and in an accompanying diagram. The force of gravity at the earth's surface gives a falling body an acceleration of 32 ft. per sec. per sec. This is $1g$.

Normal behaviour on earth	$1g$
Difficult to walk and climb	$2g$
Difficult to crawl—muscular sag	$3g$
Difficult to move	$4g$
Almost impossible to make even slight movements of arms or head	$5g$

It is interesting to compare this with the 'normal force' of gravity which a man would experience if he was on the surface of the moon or planets, which is as follows:

Moon	$0.16g$	Uranus	$1.00g$
Mercury	$0.37g$	Saturn	$1.1\ g$
Mars	$0.38g$	Neptune	$1.5\ g$
Venus	$0.86g$	Jupiter	$2.6\ g$
Earth	$1.00g$		

Thus if a man could live on the surface of any of these planets, he would feel light and able to take extraordinary movements on the moon, Mercury and Mars; on Venus, Uranus and Saturn he would feel about the same as on earth, whilst on Neptune he would begin to feel rather heavy and on Jupiter he would find walking and climbing very difficult indeed.

This applies to sustained periods of subjection to these g forces. If the forces are of shorter duration, then the effect on the human body depends on whether the man is lying in the direction of the acceleration so that his blood is forced from the head to the feet (longitudinal g), or whether he is lying so that his head and heart are at the same relative level as far as the accelerating forces are concerned (transverse g). The broad effects are these:

Longitudinal		*Transverse*	
Black-out	$3.5–8.0g$	Consciousness retained to	$17g$
Loss of consciousness	$4.0–8.5g$	Tolerable up to	$30g$
Damage to spine	above $20g$	Structural damage	above $30g$

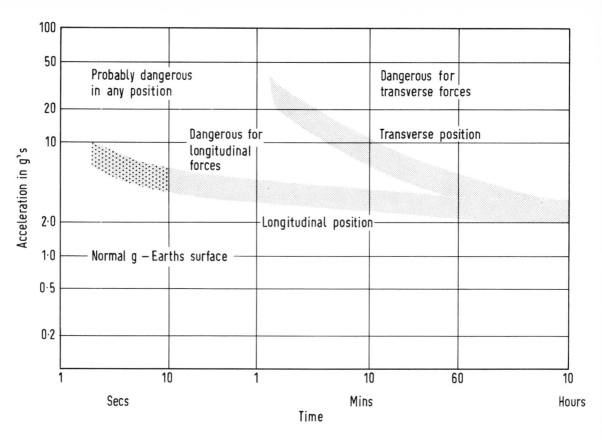

A rough indication of the probable limits of tolerance of the human being to the high accelerations and decelerations involved in rocket lift-off and re-entry from orbit. The shaded bands show the probable limits between different individuals of the black-out to unconsciousness phase with accelerations for different periods. The diagram shows that high g's which would be fatal for long periods can be tolerated for periods of seconds, and that the effect of high g depends critically on whether it acts from head to foot (i.e. driving the blood from head to feet)—longitudinal forces; or whether the forces are transverse; that is, with the heart and head at the same level relative to the accelerating force. This usually means in the prone position for the astronaut, and is clearly the correct attitude for survival under extreme conditions.

Clearly the transverse position, in which the astronaut is prone, is the correct attitude for take-off and landing.

A duplicate of Vostok was launched on two dummy runs and recovered safely, so that the planners of the flight were able to reassure themselves that as far as could be shown, their calculations were correct; and the first manned flight would be attempted. Lift-off was at 9·11 (Moscow time), and after the last stage of the rocket had fallen away over Siberia, Gagarin's words came to those who were tracking his flight on earth. 'I can see the earth in a haze. Feeling fine. How beautiful.' As he watched his instruments and carried out the necessary operations he continued to report: 'The flight is proceeding normally, and I am standing up well to the state of weightlessness.'

72

The problem of weightlessness was, of course, the opposite of the problem of the high forces during the ascent, and yet the human frame had to adapt itself from high g to zero g within minutes. Before Gagarin's flight there was extremely little available information about the reaction of the human body to a condition in which the normal gravitational forces were absent. In fact, the longest periods of weightlessness previously experienced by human beings had been for less than a minute—achieved, for example, with high-speed aircraft in special manœuvres.

Gagarin's description of the prolonged state of weightlessness was therefore of particular interest and importance: 'When the influence of gravitation began to disappear I felt excellent. Suddenly everything began to feel lighter, in general I had a sensation of unusual lightness. You know, this is a very unusual feeling. My arms and legs and my whole body felt as if they didn't belong to me. They had no weight at all. You yourself do not sit, do not lie but as it were hang suspended in the cabin. All unattached objects also hover in the air. At this time I wrote something down, only it was necessary to hold the pad with my hand, otherwise it would have sailed away. My handwriting was the same as on earth, in ordinary conditions. During this time I worked with the apparatus, in particular tapped out a radio message to earth with a telegraph key. It worked well.' (*Pravda.*) He squeezed food, in the form of a jelly, from a tube into his mouth, continued making notes and watching his instruments. With re-entry into the earth's atmosphere came the moment of greatest danger, since the deceleration loads and heating effects depend critically on a correct choice for the orientation and position of the space ship when the retro-rockets are fired. For example, the g forces involved on a space ship re-entering the earth's atmosphere from its initial orbital velocity vary tremendously with the angle at which the ship comes in as follows:

	Vertical descent	Descent at 20° to horizontal	Descent at 5° to horizontal
g force	162	55	14

This diagram indicates how the g forces vary during the descent of a space ship through the earth's atmosphere. Curve (A) is for a shallow re-entry inclined 5° to the horizontal; (B) for a steeper re-entry at an angle of about 20° to the horizontal; and (C) shows a vertical descent. The curves show that the deceleration forces increase rapidly as the steepness of the descent increases. On the other hand, the time and distance of passage through the atmosphere increases as the descent flattens. A descent like (C) would take less than a minute whereas (A) might take 10 minutes.

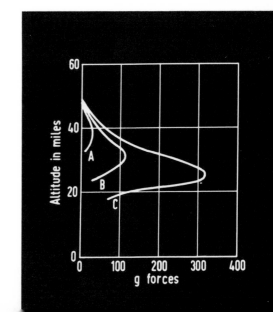

Since the heating effects increase in severity as the steepness of the descent increases, it might seem obvious that the shallowest possible re-entry path should be chosen. However, the time during which the human being has to survive these extreme conditions increases with the shallowness of the re-entry path—ranging from a half-minute for a vertical descent to a passage of thousands of miles, taking 10 minutes, for the natural decay of a satellite. The choice of the re-entry trajectory is therefore a compromise between many hazards—and when the choice is made, the orientation of the vehicle, and the control of the power and duration of burning of the rockets must be carried out with precision.

In the case of the Vostok space ship the speed of 17,000 m.p.h. had to be slowed down to less than a quarter of this rate, and when the computers gave the indication that the right moment had arrived, retro-rockets were fired forward, Vostok fell nearer the earth's atmosphere whilst the feeling of weightlessness which Gagarin had experienced began to diminish as the pull of gravity asserted itself. Flares streamed past the porthole and the temperature in the cabin soared. Pressure and vibration built up, but the cooling systems operated as planned and 108 minutes after take-off Gagarin parachuted safely down in a stubble field.

The flight of the second manned space ship took place from the 7 to 8 August 1961, when Vostok II, piloted by Major Titov, completed seventeen orbits around the earth in 25 hours 18 minutes and made a successful landing near the area where Gagarin had returned to earth. The purpose of this flight was (according to a Tass report): 'To investigate the effect of protracted flight on the human organisms in orbit and subsequent descent to the earth's surface: to investigate the working capacity of a human being during protracted conditions of weightlessness.'

Vostok II was similar to Vostok I. Both space ships weighed just over $4\frac{1}{2}$ tons, and their orbits were closely similar, the apogee (or maximum distance from earth) of Gagarin's being 190 miles and of Titov's 160 miles. Titov's orbital period was 88·6 minutes and Gagarin's 89·1 minutes. In each case two-way radio communications were maintained on frequencies in the short-wave and ultra-short-wave band.

Between the launching of the two Russian manned space vehicles, the American's first man in space, Commander Sheperd, made a ballistic hop lasting 8 minutes and reaching a height of 115 miles, whilst on 20 February 1962 there was tremendous excitement when the Redstone rocket carrying Colonel Glenn in another Mercury capsule lifted off, and millions of listeners and viewers on radios and televisions all over the world could follow his progress. Detailed commentaries from Mercury Control and observers dealing with different aspects of the flight, as well as Glenn's own voice, made the occasion one of great interest and excitement. After three orbits the capsule Friendship VII

The capsule, in which Colonel Glenn made his space flight
on 20 February 1962, arriving at the Science Museum in
London, where it was placed on exhibition. Friendship VII
weighed 2,987 lb. It was in space for 4 hours 56 minutes, during
which time it made three circuits of the earth in an orbit which
at its most distant part was 160 miles from earth and at its closest
98 miles.

made its descent into the ocean as planned. Three months later Londoners had
the opportunity to examine this historic vehicle with the marks of searing heat
left on the exterior.

On 24 May, Commander Scott Carpenter successfully undertook another
orbital flight in the Mercury capsule Aurora VII, and the duration of the flights
was extended by Commander Schirra, who made six orbits in the capsule Sigma
VII on 3 October 1962.

In between these two American manned flights the Russians surprised the
world again on 11 August by launching Major Nikolayev in Vostok III for a
prolonged flight of several days. The next day Colonel Popovich was launched
in Vostok IV with such precision that he entered his orbit within a few miles of
Vostok III. There was much speculation as to the possibility that the astronauts
had attempted manœuvres of their space craft in order to bring about a
rendezvous, but on the whole it seems likely that this episode was designed to
test the communication between two space ships in orbit, and to assess the
problems of visibility in space. In any event, during the succeeding days
Vostok III and IV separated in the way to be expected from their slightly
differing orbital periods, and both astronauts were returned safely to earth
within 5 minutes of each other on 15 August. Nikolayev had been in space for

96 hours and Popovich for 72 hours. In the first few months of 1963 both countries improved still further on these performances. The Americans launched Major Cooper on 15 May, who remained in orbit for a day and night. On 14 June the Russians launched Colonel Bykorsky in Vostok V, and he was joined 24 hours later by the world's first woman cosmonaut Valentina Terescova. Both cosmonauts returned safely to earth on 19 June.

THE FUTURE OF MAN IN SPACE

It is clear that both Russia and America are forging ahead with plans to land men on the moon. The vast sum of money allocated to the project called *Apollo* in America is indicative of the urge to get an American on the moon before a Russian. The target date set by President Kennedy is 1967, and some authorities estimate that by that time the programme could have cost 20,000 million dollars. The intention is to place a space craft containing three men into an orbit around the moon, and detach from this a two-man capsule for the lunar landing and subsequent return to the mother craft and thence to earth. Enormous problems are involved, particularly those of a successful rendezvous of two space craft in orbit and the protection of human beings from the solar radiation which they will experience in space.

The problem of the protection of astronauts from radiation in space was always recognised as a potentially serious issue. Before any space flights were made it was believed that the only serious problem would be set by the presence of cosmic rays, or high-speed protons and nuclei of the heavy atoms, which were incident on the atmosphere from outer space. Then the discovery of the large numbers of protons and electrons in the van Allen zones surrounding the earth gave rise to further anxieties. Indeed, the damage done to the solar cells of satellites orbiting in these regions of space indicate that there is foundation for such concern. However, none of the astronauts has yet been high enough to penetrate into the danger zones, and even for flight far away from the earth the astronaut would only spend a very short time in passing through the zones. No doubt at the moment the greatest need of protection in space is likely to arise because of the occasional outbursts of protons from the sun. The effects of these solar bursts and the possibility of providing astronauts with adequate protection against them is now the subject of intense study.

No details are known of the Russians' programme, although it can be safely assumed that they will not lack in determination to land a Russian on the moon before an American. Indeed the flights of Vostok III and IV are probably the first stages of an attempted rendezvous in space which seems likely to be an essential aspect of manned journeys to the moon and beyond.

Some people, even although they are enthusiastic about space research, think that the manned lunar programmes are a waste of money. They think that the results could be obtained equally well by landing unmanned space craft on the moon. This view overlooks the fact that only Man has the brain with which to deal with unexpected situations and to manipulate his apparatus to take account of the results of the investigation as it proceeds. The proper and accurate investigation of the moon is of extreme importance because it contains the history of 4,500 million years of development of the solar system on its surface features, untouched by the erosion of wind and rain which alter the surface features of the earth in periods of 10 to 50 million years. Hence there are valid scientific arguments for the manned lunar programme as well as tremendous propaganda

An indication of the probable limits for exposure for a human being to radiation. The two lower bands give the limit for genetical damage for peak and accumulated doses. The vertical scale is in röntgens (r)—the unit which specifies the amount of irradiation, by X-rays and gamma rays, to which an organism has been exposed. The dose in röntgens is proportional to the duration of the exposure and to the intensity. The diagram below indicates that without suffering genetical damage, a human being can absorb say 5 r a year continually or up to 15 r in any one year as a peak dose. If genetical damage is suffered, the organism can stand much heavier doses as indicated in the top band. An acute dose of about 600 r over a short period of time is believed to be lethal. Thus in the outer van Allen zone it is estimated that an unshielded astronaut would receive a dose equivalent to about 10 r an hour, which would represent a lethal dose if he stayed there for 2 or 3 days.

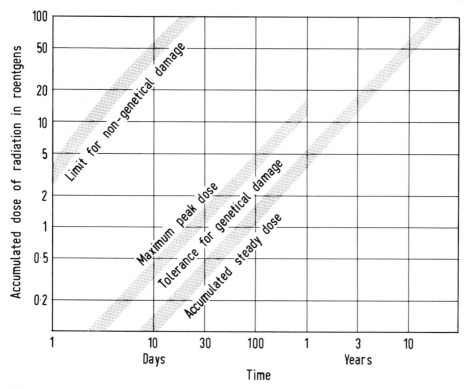

and military aspects in being first on the lunar terrain. But after all, the incentive of discovery and exploration has been one of the driving forces in the development of Man. Since the journey of a man to the moon is one of the greatest challenges which has ever faced the human race, it seems likely that Man will be impelled towards this goal regardless of those who consider that it would be better to spend the money on earth.

[*Opposite*]   A diagrammatic illustration issued by the United States of their intended stages preliminary to the landing of a man on the moon. The Mercury manned flights with one man in orbit for less than a day will be succeeded by the Gemini space craft which will orbit the earth with two men for much longer periods, and in 1964 will be used to test the 'docking', or rendezvous, procedures whereby units of a space craft may be joined together while in orbit around the earth. This rendezvous procedure is essential for the lunar Apollo programme. The intention is to place the main Apollo space craft, containing three men, in an orbit around the earth for periods up to 2 weeks in 1965. This is Apollo A. The next stage, Apollo B, is planned for 1966 and involves a manned journey around the moon, without landing, and returning to earth. The final stage of the programme, Apollo C, scheduled for 1967–70, involves the landing of two men on the moon. It is intended to do this by placing the main Apollo space craft with its three men in an orbit around the moon. A smaller craft containing two of the men will then detach itself from the parent craft and land on the moon. After spending some time on the lunar surface these two men will launch themselves into a lunar orbit, rendezvous with the parent craft, and then return to earth.

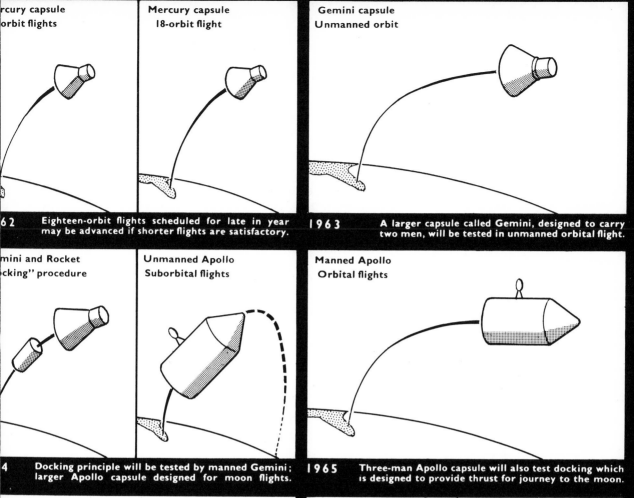

Mercury capsule
orbit flights

Mercury capsule
18-orbit flight

Gemini capsule
Unmanned orbit

62 Eighteen-orbit flights scheduled for late in year may be advanced if shorter flights are satisfactory.

1963 A larger capsule called Gemini, designed to carry two men, will be tested in unmanned orbital flight.

mini and Rocket
ocking" procedure

Unmanned Apollo
Suborbital flights

Manned Apollo
Orbital flights

4 Docking principle will be tested by manned Gemini; larger Apollo capsule designed for moon flights.

1965 Three-man Apollo capsule will also test docking which is designed to provide thrust for journey to the moon.

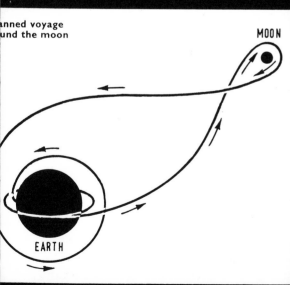

anned voyage
und the moon

MOON

EARTH

6 Manned Apollo flight will be made around moon. Rocket will fire craft out of earth orbit into Lunar course.

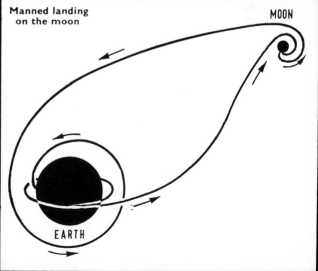

Manned landing
on the moon

MOON

EARTH

1967-70 Manned landing will be made on moon in Apollo capsule which will carry rockets for return flight to earth.

7 Radio telescopes and the solar system

The techniques of radio astronomy and the space probe are already contributing to a spectacular increase in our knowledge of the solar system, particularly of the moon and the planets. In this chapter we shall give one or two examples of the new ideas which are being introduced by these researches.

THE MOON

Ten years ago it was a difficult technological problem to transmit radio waves from earth and pick them up again $2\frac{1}{2}$ seconds later after they had been reflected from the surface of the moon, nearly a quarter of a million miles away. Today, with the large radio telescopes, this is an easy task, but unexpected effects have been encountered. If radio waves of uniform strength are transmitted they are scattered from the lunar surface, but the signals collected as echoes on a cathode-ray tube are not always of the same strength. Very marked irregularities in the strength of the returned echoes are found, even in the pulses separated in time by only a second or so. There is also a long period variation in the average strength of returned signals with periods of 15 or 30 minutes. It has been found that the two effects are separate phenomena.

The long-period variation is the result of the influence of the earth's magnetic field on the radio waves as they traverse the space between moon and earth. The effect occurs principally in the ionosphere of the earth at a height of 100–300 miles. Systematic measurements of this fading have provided a method of assessing the total number of electrons between the earth and moon.

The short-period fading in periods of seconds is quite a different effect caused by the libration of the moon. Due to slight irregularities in the motion of the moon around the earth, it never presents exactly the same face, but gives the effect of a slight oscillation, known as libration. Thus the parts of the lunar surface reflecting the radio waves to earth are constantly changing, and this causes large variations in the strength of the signal returned to earth. The mathematical analysis of these fluctuations gave a most important result. Whereas in the case of the reflection of light the moon scatters in the same way as a sphere of chalk (that is, it appears to be uniformly bright), yet when radio waves are directed towards it the scattering is similar to that of a polished ball-bearing in a beam of light—namely the central region of the ball appears brighter than the remainder of the surface. Thus the radio waves scattered from the moon seem to come predominantly from a small part of the forward hemisphere.

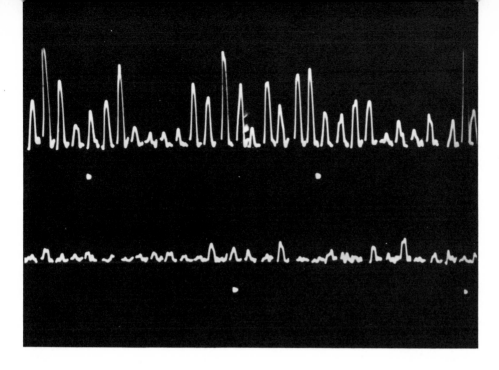

Photographs of a cathode-ray tube displaying radio echoes from the moon. In this experiment the radio telescope at Jodrell Bank was equipped with a transmitter which beamed on to the moon pulses of radio waves separated by 1·8 seconds. After 2·5 seconds the pulse of radio waves was received again by the radio telescope, having been scattered from the lunar surface nearly a quarter of a million miles distant. Although the pulses transmitted were of equal strength, those received back on earth fluctuated markedly as shown in this illustration. In the top section the returned echoes are strong, but they show rapid changes in strength from echo to echo. As explained in the text, this effect is caused by the apparent 'rocking' or libration of the moon. The bottom section was recorded 14 minutes before the top section. The pulse to pulse fluctuation is still apparent, but in addition the mean strength of the echoes is considerably decreased. These longer period changes of the intensity are introduced as the radio waves traverse the earth's atmosphere. The white dots on these records are half-minute time marks.

An interesting practical result of this discovery has been the use of the moon as a means of bouncing radio messages from one side of the earth to the other, using wave-lengths so short that the earth's ionosphere was penetrated, and therefore no interference from sun-spots need be anticipated. At first it was believed that this novel method of communication would not be feasible because the moon, reflecting over so large an area, would introduce so great an amount of distortion as to render the signals unintelligible. However, the conclusion reached from the study of the short-period fading seemed to remove this obstacle, and an attempt to modulate the radio waves going out from the radio telescope with speech proved successful. A tape recording of the scientist at Jodrell Bank calling 'Good night, good night, good night' to the moon, answered by three echoing good nights is among the archives of first occasions.

There seems little doubt that many important questions can only be answered by carrying instruments to the moon in space probes as described in Chapter 5. Lunik II crashed its instruments on the moon's surface, but we may expect before long that control in the final stages of flight will make a soft landing possible, so that instruments will remain in working order on the lunar surface. This would make it possible to study the atmosphere and magnetic field (if any) and make detailed measurements of the nature of the surface, particularly the composition and properties of the lunar crust, the surface temperature and its variation with time and depth, surface radioactivity, and seismic properties of the lunar interior. Untouched by the erosion of wind and rain, the lunar surface must contain evidence of aeons of history. Is there an identity of material between the meteorites which crash to earth and the lunar surface? In the United States Professor Urey's analysis of certain meteorites seemed to indicate that at some stage they must have gone through a process of heating such as could only occur in the interior of a body at least the size of the moon. He has suggested that at some stage in the evolution of the solar system there were a number of bodies like the moon in orbit around the sun, and that these collided with one another and were shattered in the process. In this case the meteorites which reach the earth might be some of the pieces of these moon-like bodies. It will be most important to find out if the analysis of the lunar surface, made by instruments in the probes which will soon land on it, give results indicating that the meteorites might have originated in this way.

THE PLANETS

Although the lunar radar experiments are quite easily carried out with the modern large radio telescopes, this type of experiment with the nearer planets is far more difficult. The moon is 240,000 miles away, so that the return journey of the radio waves from earth takes only $2\frac{1}{2}$ seconds. At its closest approach Venus is 25 million miles away, so the signal would take over 4 minutes on the journey there and back, and success is 10 million times more difficult to achieve in terms of sensitivity of apparatus than in the moon experiments.

Attempts have been made by an American team with a very powerful transmitter on an 80-ft. radio telescope, and a team at Jodrell Bank using a smaller transmitter in the 250-ft. radio telescope, and both have achieved success. A direct measurement of the distance of the planet from earth has been made. This is most significant because it leads immediately to a value for the solar parallax—that is, the angle subtended by the earth's equatorial radius at the sun. This parallax is fundamental to the scale of the solar system, and indeed the earth–sun distance, known as the 'astronomical unit', is the base from which the distances of the stars are measured. Many attempts have been made by optical methods to determine the solar parallax accurately, but they have given divergent results. Now it seems that the direct radar measurement of the

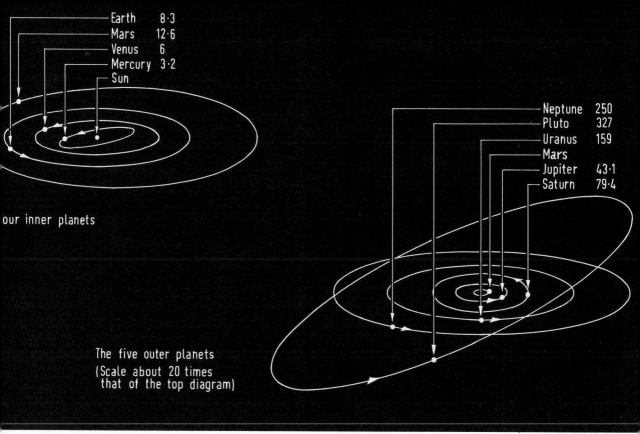

Earth 8·3
Mars 12·6
Venus 6
Mercury 3·2
Sun

our inner planets

Neptune 250
Pluto 327
Uranus 159
Mars
Jupiter 43·1
Saturn 79·4

The five outer planets
(Scale about 20 times
that of the top diagram)

The planets of the solar system. The numbers give the mean distance of the orbit of the planet from the sun in light-minutes. (Thus sun–earth distance=8·3 light-minutes=8·3×60×186,000=93,000,000 miles.) Other physical data about the planetary system follows:

	Period of rotation around the sun, i.e. length of year	Period of rotation on axis, i.e. length of day	Mass-taking earth=1 (=6×10²¹ tons)	Radius in miles	Approximate temperature on sunlit side
Mercury	88 days	88 days	0·05	1,500	340° C.
Venus	225 days	uncertain may be 225 days	0·81	3,900	100° C. (uncertain)
Earth	365 days	24 hours	1	4,000	22° C.
Mars	1·9 years	24·6 hours	0·11	2,100	−13° C.
Jupiter	12 years	10 hours	318	45,000	−130° C.
Saturn	29 years	10 hours	95·2	37,000	−153° C.
Uranus	84 years	11 hours	14·5	15,000	(uncertain)
Neptune	165 years	16 hours	17·2	14,000	−165° C.
Pluto	248 years	16 hours	0·9	4,500	−225° C. (uncertain)

Between the orbits of Mars and Jupiter there is the belt of asteroids, or minor planets. The orbits of about 1,500 have been determined but over 6,000 have been discovered. The mean period (col. 1 above) is 4·5 years and the total mass of asteroids is about 2×10^{18} tons (i.e. about $\frac{1}{1000}$ of the earth's mass). The sizes vary from 400 miles diameter (Ceres) to only 1 mile (Hermes).

83

distance of Venus from the earth has at last provided a definitive and unambiguous value.

It is hoped that future work will enable scientists to measure the rate of rotation of the planet, and indicate something of the nature of its surface. Perhaps information about the rotation period will come first from instruments carried in the space probes described in Chapter 5, which may either orbit or make a close approach to the planet.[1]

Radio emissions from several of the planets in the region of centimetre wave-lengths have been measured by radio telescopes. These relate to the thermal emission appropriate to the body's temperature, and comparisons with temperatures derived by optical studies are being made. From Jupiter large sporadic outbursts on long wave-lengths have been observed, the energies involved being enormous. There is some evidence that these events occur on the planet's surface rather than in its atmosphere, and if this is the case, the forces at work must be equivalent to volcanic eruptions like the explosion of Krakatau or to the energies involved in several hydrogen bombs. Also in the case of Jupiter, radio emissions have been measured with properties which lead

[1] Subsequent radar work on Venus in the U.S.S.R. as well as in the U.S. and at Jodrell Bank has shown that the rotation of the planet is probably nearly the same as its orbital period around the sun, so that it always presents the same face to the sun in the way the moon presents the same face to the earth.

A meteor, or shooting star, photographed by the Jodrell Bank Schmidt camera, illustrated in Chapter 1. The regular breaks in the trail are caused by an 18-bladed rotating shutter in the camera which occults the lens. This enables the velocity with which the meteor travels across the sky to be measured. These velocities vary from 7 to 46 miles per sec., and their accurate measurement, together with that of the direction of the meteor, is needed so that information about the path of the meteor in space may be obtained before it enters the earth's atmosphere. The many short background streaks in this photograph are star trails caused by the rotation of the camera on the earth during the exposure. This particular meteor would have been seen as a bright streak by the naked eye in the dark sky, lasting for about a second. The mass of the particle which burnt up in the atmosphere to produce this shooting star must have been about one-tenth of a gramme (about three thousandths of an ounce) and the size of a pin-head. Something like a million particles per day of this size burn up in the earth's atmosphere. As the particles get smaller (and the shooting stars fainter), their numbers increase, until at the limit of visibility of the naked eye (about 100 times fainter than the meteor in this photograph) the earth collects several hundred millions per day.

us to believe that they originate in radiation belts around the planet, like the van Allen zones around the earth.

METEORS OR SHOOTING STARS

Radio astronomy, as early as 1946, was providing a method for the study of meteors which overcame the obscuring effects of cloud, moonlight or daylight. The presence of meteors had been observed for centuries, both the sporadic meteors, which seemed to be distributed fairly uniformly in interplanetary space, and the shower meteors which appeared to radiate from a particular point in the sky, and generally occurred regularly from year to year at the same time, when the normal nightly rate rose from 10 to 50 or 100 per hour. From whence did they come? The earth, moving in orbit around the sun at a speed of 19 miles per sec., occasionally runs into streams of debris concentrated in orbits round the sun, which enter its atmosphere and give rise to meteor showers. In many cases these concentrations are closely associated with comets. They move under gravitational control within the solar system, and their nucleus is an icy conglomerate of various carbon compounds, whilst in most cases a long tail streams behind the head for millions of kilometres. (The sight of these in the night sky was said to be an omen of disaster in distant ages, and their appearance

The systematic studies of meteors have been revolutionised by the techniques of radio astronomy. When a meteor burns up in the high atmosphere it leaves behind a transient trail of ionised particles which reflect energy from a radio wave beamed on to the trail from a radio telescope. The returned signal is analogous to a radar echo from an aircraft, and the meteor trail gives an echo on a cathode-ray tube in the same way as the aircraft. Four meteor echoes are shown in this photograph. At (A) the echoes are displayed as a single vertical deflection of the tube trace. This deflection is generally transient (one-tenth of a second, more rarely several seconds), and from it the range of the meteor can be measured. At (B) the time-base has been speeded up so that the individual pulses (600 per sec.) are now spaced. From the pattern the velocity of the meteor can be measured. At (C) and (D) the drift of the trail either away from or towards the station on earth can be measured. The great advantage of the radio techniques has been that the meteors can be studied by day or when the sky is cloudy, and that it is so sensitive that accurate measurements can be made on meteors which are far below the limit of visibility. The four meteors in this photograph, recorded at Jodrell Bank, were all well below the visibility limit—minute particles weighing less than a thousandth of a gramme. The earth collects several thousand million particles of this size every day.

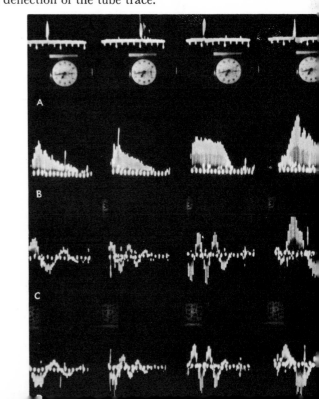

85

nearly always had dramatic associations.) In the tail are large numbers of small specks of dust, possibly evaporated from the nucleus as the comet approached the sun. In October 1946 the earth crossed the orbit of the Giacobini-Zinner comet only a few days distance from the position of its nucleus. Between midnight and 6 a.m. on 10 October thousands of meteors were observed, although both before and after only the normal number were seen. This provided a clear and spectacular contemporary demonstration of the close relationship between meteors and comets.

Until 1946 the systematic study of meteors was severely handicapped by skies which were either too cloudy or made too light by the moon, but with the advent of radio astronomy these difficulties were overcome. The meteoric particle evaporating in the high atmosphere leaves behind it a trail of ionised particles as well as the visual streak of light. As the electrons in this ionised trail are efficient scatterers of radio waves, a beam may be directed towards them from a radio telescope, and the returning signal detected as a transient echo by the receiving part of the equipment. With further development in meteor studies by space probes and satellites on the micro-meteorites as described in Chapter 4, together with ground-based photographic and radio echo work on the meteors which burn up in the atmosphere, there will be a better understanding of the role of these particles in the formation and evolution of the solar system. At present it is thought that the large meteorites which fall to earth have a different

Many of the shooting stars seen in the sky at night appear to come from all directions. These are the sporadic meteors, and accurate measurements show that they are in fact approximately uniformly distributed. Occasionally a different phenomenon manifests itself. The number of meteors increases considerably and measurements show that they are entering the atmosphere along parallel paths from a definite 'radiant point' in the sky. These are the 'shower meteors' which occur when the earth passes through a stream of meteoric debris also moving in orbit around the sun as shown in this diagram. These showers may last for a few nights until the earth emerges from the debris. Some of the showers are quite regular in occurrence—such as the Perseids, which occur every year in the first part of August (reaching a maximum on 10–14 August), the Geminids which appear in December, and the Quadrantids in early January. The showers are named after the constellation in the sky from which they appear to emerge. Some other showers, like the Giacobinids in October or the Leonids in November, have given enormous displays of meteors in the past, but the main debris has now been deflected away from the earth's orbit. These meteor showers are closely related to comets; in some cases the comet no longer exists; in others, such as the Giacobinid shower, both meteors and comets are present today.

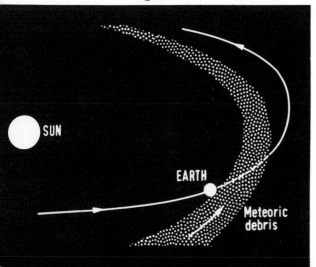

SUN

EARTH

Meteoric
debris

86

The Giacobini-Zinner comet photographed at the Lick Observatory, California, on 27 September 1946. The streaks in the photograph are star trails caused by the movement of the earth during the exposure. This comet was discovered in 1900. On 10 October 1946 (13 days after this photograph was obtained) the earth crossed the orbit of the comet 15 days behind the passage of the comet itself, and a great shower of meteors was observed. The orbits of over 500 comets are known with some accuracy. Some move around the sun with a period of a few years, but many were believed to be transient visitors from interstellar space. Nowadays it is thought that these are moving in very long period elliptical orbits, and that all comets are members of the solar system. The nucleus of the comet is an icy conglomerate of small solid particles frozen in gas. As it approaches the sun some of this gas evaporates and a long tail is produced, so tenuous that it always points away from the sun—'blown' by the pressure of sunlight. The precise part which comets play in the evolution of the solar system is a matter of great uncertainty.

origin from the meteors. Questions as to whether the meteorites form a separate class, or are an extension of the size range of meteors, and whether all this debris represents samples of primeval material left over from the formation of the solar system, or is the consequence of some planetary catastrophe, are still un-answered.

The sun, parent of the solar system, has a diameter of 865,000 miles (excluding the solar atmosphere) and its mass is 332,000 times greater than that of the earth. Its weight is approximately 10^{27} tons; that is, a thousand billion billion tons. Its energy output, produced by converting 4 million tons of solar matter into energy every second by thermonuclear processes, is nearly a billion billion kilowatts.

This conversion takes place in the centre of the sun where the temperature is about 20 million degrees centigrade, and the pressures amount to several thousand million atmospheres. Here atoms are stripped of electrons and matter is degenerate. These transmutations in the sun's interior involve the conversion of 564 million tons of hydrogen to 560 million tons of helium every second. Although the material is being used at this rate, the processes have already been in operation for at least 4,000 million years. However, the sun's mass is so tremendous that this rate of use of its material represents only one-tenth per cent of its mass every 10,000 million years.

Observations of the solar surface through optical instruments indicate a temperature of about 6,000° C. and a number of variable features. The most striking of these are the sun-spots, which were first observed by Galileo, and whose appearance on the disk varies in an eleven-year cycle. They appear to be cooler than their surroundings, and may start as circular whirlpools occurring high up in the solar atmosphere, later twisting as they drift towards the sun's equator, but even today their exact origin and nature is imperfectly understood.

Occasionally, where a large group of sun-spots is observed, a solar flare occurs, accompanied by a violent ejection of hydrogenous material. Man's study

A solar prominence photographed at the Yerkes Observatory in the United States. These prominences are gigantic eruptions of the solar chromosphere and generally occur in the disturbed regions associated with groups of sun-spots. They consist of hot, tenuous gases at temperatures of more than 10,000 degrees, which are thrown

high above the solar atmosphere. In many cases it appears that the gases are constrained by the solar magnetic field and return to the solar surface in a great arch as shown in this photograph. In these cases the gas may be thrown over 100,000 miles above the solar surface before it subsides back into the sun. Occasionally the explosion is so violent that the gas is ejected completely from the sun.

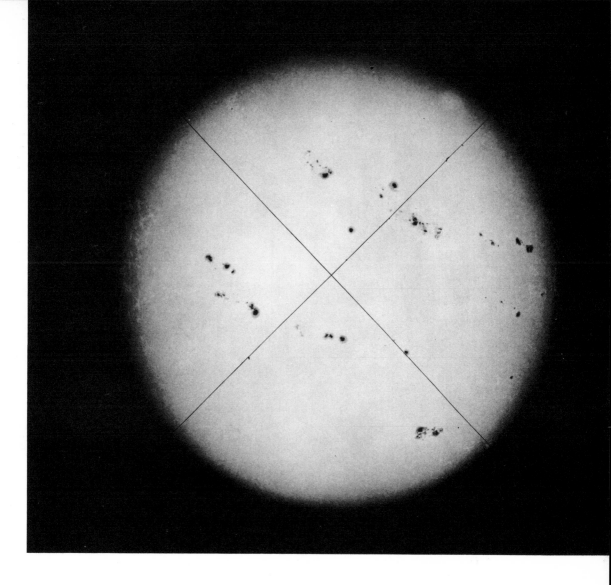

A photograph taken at the Royal Greenwich Observatory in 1947 showing large
numbers of sun-spots on the solar disk. The sun-spots appear in maximum numbers
in an eleven-year cycle, and this photograph was taken during one of the epochs
of maximum. The most recent maximum of the solar cycle in 1957–8 was the
occasion of the International Geophysical Year in which there was a co-ordinated
world-wide measurement of many geophysical phenomena influenced by solar
conditions—such as the earth's ionosphere. Small sun-spots may be a few thousand
miles across and last for a few days, while large sun-spots may last for months.
One of the largest spots on record—covering 7,000 million sq. miles of the solar
surface—occurred during the 1947 maximum. They rotate with the sun (this was
the first method by which the sun's rotation period was measured and found to be
27 days)—hence some large spots survive for more than a complete rotation of the
sun. It is generally believed that the sun-spots occur in the form of a vortex in
the atmosphere of the sun associated with locally intense magnetic fields, but
there is no complete understanding of the phenomena—or of the reasons for the
appearance of the spots in maximum numbers every eleven years.

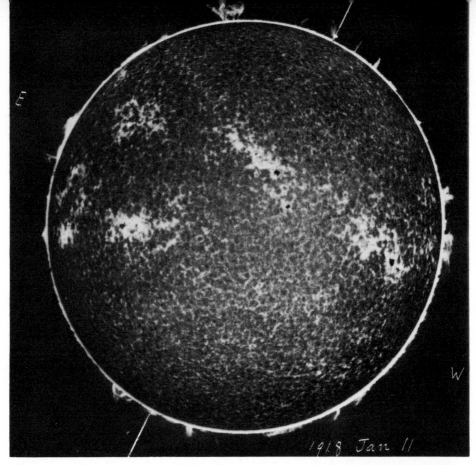

The most spectacular solar events are the great flares in which, during the course of a few minutes, a thousand million square miles of the sun's atmosphere may suddenly increase in brilliance by ten times. The flare is made up of a complicated series of white hot filaments of gas which, although they flare up so quickly, may take an hour or more to decay. The time of appearance of flares is unpredictable, although they are always associated with complicated groups of sun-spots. During the most intense phase of a flare major prominences occur and great streams of hydrogen gas are blown away from the sun. Some of this material takes 24 hours to travel through space to the neighbourhood of the earth and gives rise to marked terrestrial effects—severe magnetic storms and auroral phenomena. The ionosphere is also disturbed by the intense ultra-violet radiations created during the flare, and it is these disturbances which interfere with long-distance radio communications.

of these events with spectro-helioscopes and other optical instruments has now been extended by the use of radio telescopes, and one of the first discoveries made with the new instruments of radio astronomy was that sun-spots, particularly on occasions when a large flare occurred, generated powerful radio waves. Many types of intense sporadic emissions were observed, associated with disturbances on the solar surface.

Radio waves, generated by the corona—the attenuated atmosphere—of the sun are weaker, but present all the time. The vast gaseous layer of the corona,

During an eclipse when the sun is obscured by the moon the halo, or corona, of
the sun's atmosphere is visible. Even near the limb of the sun the intensity of the
light from this corona is only a millionth part of the brightness of the sun, and
for a long time our only knowledge of the corona came from the occasional
transient observations which could be made during a total eclipse. Then, in 1930,
the French astronomer Professor Lyot perfected a camera known as a coronagraph,
with which it was possible to photograph the corona at any time. The shape and
extent of the corona varies during the sun-spot cycle, and occasionally streams
from the corona can be traced out to several solar radii. In fact, the modern
conception, which has been developed on the basis of the measurements in radio
astronomy and the space probes, is that this corona—in a highly attenuated form—
streams out and envelops the earth. The gas of the corona which is visible in
the photographs is ionised and at an effective temperature of a million degrees.
The mechanism by which the gas is maintained at this temperature above the
solar surface (which is only at 6,000°) is not well understood. One suggestion is
that it is heated by the passage of electric currents which pass through the gas, but
begin and end in the chromosphere. Another idea is that the heating is caused
by the capture of the interstellar dust which the sun sweeps up in its journey
through space. In this photograph of the corona a large prominence can be seen
on the limb of the sun.

streaming out to several solar radii, may be seen during the sun's eclipse, and is always in a state of turbulent motion. At a distance of half a solar radius above the visible disk, there are 30 million atoms per c.cm., and the effective temperature is a few million degrees absolute. Recent calculations indicate a resultant outward pressure causing this coronal material to expand continuously at a speed between 300 and 900 miles per sec. This streaming material is known as the solar wind, and further experimental evidence of its existence was provided when the Americans launched a space probe in the spring of 1961, equipped with specialised detecting and measuring instruments. The operation was successful, though the probe only remained in space for 48 hours. It is now believed that during periods of sun-spots and solar flares the speed of ejection of the material of the corona and chromosphere is increased by several times.

It may be that gas in a highly ionised condition, like the material of the solar wind, moving in interplanetary space, carries with it its own magnetic field. This concept of ionised particles and magnetic field moving together through the solar system, and in other parts of the cosmos, has become of great importance in astrophysical theory.

In the case of the gas streaming from the sun, carrying its own magnetic field, a disturbance of the earth's environment results from the injection of these

When the sun is disturbed by sun-spots and flares it becomes a powerful emitter of radio waves. This record shows how the intensity of the radio emission from the sun increases rapidly within a few minutes during such an outburst and may take several hours to return to its normal value. It is quite common for the strength of these radio outbursts to be 100 times greater than the radio emission which comes from the sun in its quiet condition, and some exceptional solar flares have produced an intensity of radio emission 10,000 times greater than the normal value. A considerable literature has accumulated since the Second World War on these solar radio

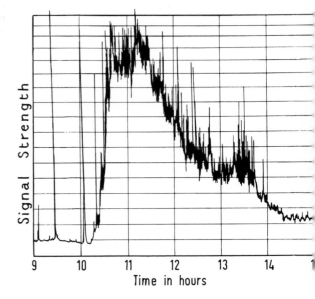

emissions and their relations to the various solar disturbances observed visually. The strength of the radio signals is so large compared with those recorded from the galaxy that their investigation can be carried out with relatively simple equipment.

electrons into the earth's magnetic field. Here they become trapped, and in this way the outer layer of the van Allen zones is probably formed. Herein may lie an explanation of the partial disappearance of these outer zones during a magnetic storm, and their subsequent repopulation with electrons in the succeeding days. In principle, a fairly solid barrier against injection of low energy particles from outside should be provided by the earth's magnetic field, but its distortion by travelling fields, coming away from the sun, facilitate the injection.

The aurora borealis, or northern lights, for long associated with solar flares, were believed to be caused by particles streaming out from the region of the flare and approaching earth after 24–36 hours, when they entered the atmosphere and gave rise to ionisation at a height of about 60 miles. This theory cannot be correct since now we know that the particles from the sun are trapped in the outer van Allen zone. It seems more likely that the primary aurora particles originate in the outer zone, and the function of the magnetic storm is

During a solar flare violent ejections of the hydrogen gas of the solar atmosphere take place, and these travel through space, enveloping the earth from 24 to 36 hours after ejection. It is now believed that this 'plasma' carries its own magnetic field with it, since it is a good conductor and pulls out the lines of magnetic force from the sun with it. Its roots remain in the sun, and the solar protons spiral around the lines of force as shown in this diagram. This modern concept explains the complicated terrestrial disturbances which follow solar flares, and also a remarkable

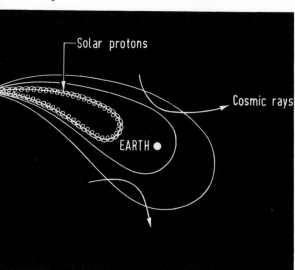

new phenomenon discovered in the space probe Pioneer V. For many years it has been known that the cosmic rays measured on earth decreased in intensity when there was a magnetic storm following a solar flare; this was thought to be caused by the local influence of the earth's changing magnetic field on the cosmic rays. When Pioneer V was several million miles away from earth a great magnetic storm occurred, whereupon the cosmic-ray intensity decreased in Pioneer V simultaneously with the decrease on earth. This showed that the effect was general in the solar system and not localised to the earth. The concept of the travelling magnetic field frozen in the plasma provides a ready explanation since, as shown in the diagram, the cosmic rays will be deflected by the field of the plasma and the effect is not specifically associated with the local change of the earth's magnetic field.

to produce the magnetically disturbed condition which allows the particles to escape from this zone and enter the atmosphere along the earth's own magnetic lines of force.

As well as the powerful emissions of radio waves during sun-spots, there are also less intense radio emissions from the solar corona. If we imagine viewing the sun with radio eyes, instead of with our normal eyes, than at a wave-length of 21 cm. the appearance of the sun would be of a flattened disk, much brighter towards the edges than in the centre. This would take the place of the familiar optical view of a uniform disk. Viewed at longer wave-lengths in the metre

[*Below*]   The aurora borealis, or northern lights, photographed by the famous Norwegian scientist Professor Störmer in 1947 near Oslo. The lower border of this aurora was about 60 miles above the earth, and although the aurorae occasionally extend to much greater heights, the majority are concentrated at a height of 60–80 miles. The aurora is formed by the impact of particles from space which ionise the atoms of the atmosphere. These particles are now believed to come from the outer regions of the van Allen zones of trapped particles. In polar latitudes the aurora is a common sight, but at lower latitudes its appearance is more closely associated with violent solar activity, giving rise to large magnetic storms on earth.

wave-band, it would seem that the sun monopolised much of the sky. On wave-lengths of several metres the 'radio sun' has been traced out to between 20 and 30 solar radii. This means that the influence of the solar atmosphere extends through great distances of interplanetary space; an entirely fresh conception arising directly from work with the new tools of radio astronomy and the space probe.

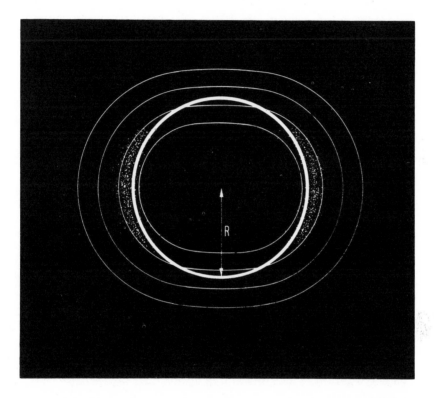

When the sun is undisturbed by spots or flares the radio emission comes predominantly from the corona, but the shape of the sun seen by the radio telescopes is not circular, as we observe it visually. In this diagram the thick circle is the normal outline of the solar chromosphere (which we see by eye) and (R) is the normal solar radius. When the sun is observed on short radio wave-lengths (say 60 cm. or less) the radiation comes from the corona at radii slightly greater than (R), but this radio sun is not uniformly bright like the visual sun. It is limb brightened—that is, in the places shaded the radio emission is more intense than from the remainder of the corona. Also the shape is not circular—it is flattened at the poles as indicated by the line contours. As the wave-length of observation increases, the sun may be observed with a radio telescope out to greater and greater distances from the visible disk. At very long wave-lengths this radio corona has been observed out to 100 solar radii.

8 Our own galaxy

THE MILKY WAY SYSTEM

The stars in our own galaxy are contained in a flattened disk-like structure. This star system which we call the Milky Way extends for 100,000 light-years into space. Near the central regions, or nucleus, the disk is a few thousand light-years thick. The system contains great clouds of dust lying in the plane, which obscure the astronomer's view of the central regions, for he and his telescopes on earth are situated far out in one of the spiral arms. Only a microscopic speck of dust exists in every few cubic centimetres of space, but the volumes of space are so tremendous that the cumulative effect of this obscuration means that 99 per cent of starlight fails to reach us. For the radio astronomer, however, no such hindrance exists, and his radio telescopes can pierce to these hitherto obscured central parts. In this chapter we describe some of the new facts which have been revealed about our own galaxy by the radio telescopes.

RADIO EMISSIONS FROM SPACE

In Chapter 2, where the early attempts to make a radio map of the sky were described, it was mentioned that the strength of the radio waves picked up in the narrow beam of a radio telescope varied as it was pointed to different parts of the heavens. It appeared that these signals differed in accordance with the concentration of visible stars, but individual stars did not contribute to the emission. As the beam moved over the galactic plane, the signal strength increased slowly, with a sharp rise within a degree of so of the plane. Scans at different galactic longitudes showed the strongest signals coming from the nucleus, where the concentration of visible stars was greatest. But the apparent obvious explanation of this, that stars emit both radio signals and light, is not correct because when the radio telescope is pointed at bright stars like Sirius or Capella, no radio waves are detected (at least by present techniques). There must be some other explanation, and our present belief is that the peak of radio intensity in the region of the galactic plane is the result of radio waves emitted by four different processes. (1) By the neutral interstellar hydrogen gas. (2) By the hydrogen gas which is ionised in the vicinity of hot stars. (3) By the motion of high-speed electrons in the magnetic field of the galaxy (synchrotron emission). (4) By localised or discrete sources of radio emission some of which have been identified optically. In the following sections a brief description will be given of these processes.

[continued on page 99]

This diagram illustrates the probable arrangement of the stars in the local galaxy or Milky Way system. The 100,000 million stars which comprise the system are arranged in a flattened disk as at (a). The dimensions of the star system are such that starlight takes 100,000 years to traverse the disk; that is, the system extends for 100,000 light-years. In the dense central regions the thickness increases to about 20,000 light-years. The sun, an average type of star, is 30,000 light-years from the central regions. When viewed from above, the galaxy would have the type of structure shown in (b). The stars are not uniformly distributed in the plane of the disk, but are arranged in spiral arms emerging from the nucleus of the system. If it were possible to photograph the galaxy from a remote part of the universe looking down on the disk it would be similar to M51 in the photograph shown on page 103. Photographed 'end-on' from a great distance its appearance would be like that of M104 on page 98 in which the dust in the plane of the galaxy obscures the starlight. This is indicated by the line across the plane in (a) below.

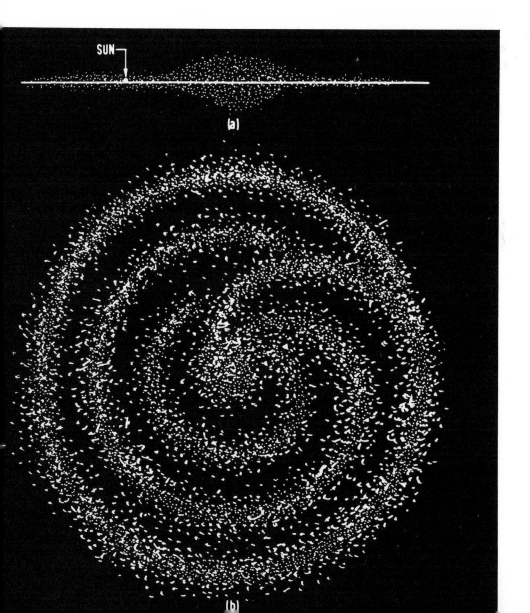

SUN

(a)

(b)

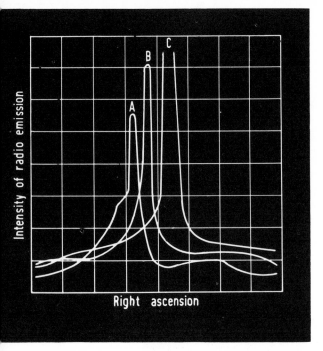

Intensity of radio emission

Right ascension

[*Left*] This diagram, which was obtained with a high definition radio telescope in Sydney working on a wave-length of $3\frac{1}{2}$ metres, shows how the strength of the radio emission changes as the telescope is directed to different parts of the galaxy. In each case (*A, B, C*) the telescope is moved across the plane of the galaxy (for example, in (*a*) on page 97 the telescope beam would be moving vertically across the diagram), and it is obvious that the strength of the signal increases rapidly in the plane of the system where most stars are concentrated. In addition, when the telescope is directed so that the scan takes place across the plane nearer to the central regions then the strength of the peak emission increases (the progression (*A*) (*B*) (*C*)). The analysis of these and many similar curves has made possible the investigation of the complex processes by which the radio emission is generated.

[*Below*] A photograph of the galaxy M104 in Virgo about 40 million light-years away. The dark band across the galaxy is the result of the obscuration of the light of the stars in the nebula by the interstellar dust in its plane. We believe that the Milky Way system would appear like this if viewed 'end-on' from a similar distance (compare the diagrams of the Milky Way on page 97).

I. THE RADIO EMISSION FROM THE NEUTRAL HYDROGEN GAS

In the neutral state hydrogen cannot be detected optically, for to become visible, hydrogen has to be excited, so that the electrons in it can undergo transitions between different energy levels, and emit light. It was not until radio telescopes received emissions from the neutral hydrogen that its presence could be demonstrated practically. The suggestion that such radio waves could be emitted on a wave-length of 21 cm. came from a young Dutch astronomer, Van der Hulst, working on Professor Oort's staff at Leiden under war-time conditions of much danger and difficulty. In spite of the German occupation, the scientists continued to hold colloquia, and at one of these in 1944 Van der Hulst presented his theory. In the hydrogen atom the electron either spins in

[*continued on page* 102]

[*Below*]   An example of a gaseous nebula in the Milky Way. This is the Trifid nebula, M20, in Sagittarius, photographed by the 200-in. Mt Palomar telescope. The dark lanes showing in these gaseous nebulae are not due to the absence of gas. They are caused by interstellar dust which is obscuring the light of the nebula, and this dust also accounts for the irregular shapes of many of the nebulae. These regions of ionised hydrogen may be detected in radio telescopes working on short wave-lengths. It is in such regions that the 'free-free' transitions between electrons and protons occur, giving rise to the 'thermal' radio emission as described in the text.

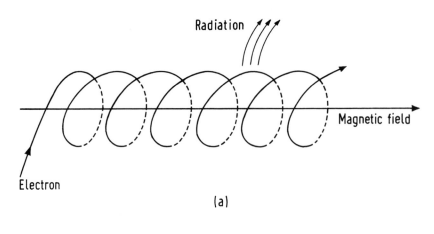

(a)

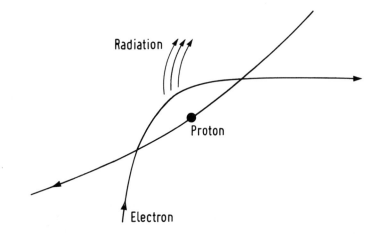

(b)

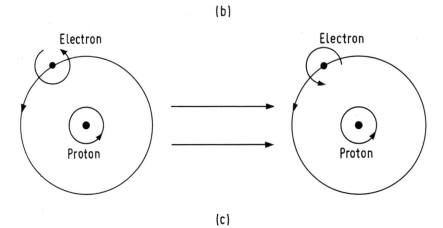

(c)

[*Opposite*]   These three diagrams illustrate the three basic processes which are believed to produce the radio emissions in the Milky Way. In (*a*) an electron moving at very high speed executes a spiral motion in the magnetic field of the galaxy. Because of its high acceleration the electron emits radiation in the radio wave part of the spectrum (in the metre wave-band). This emission occurs in the plane of the Milky Way and in the halo surrounding the main system of stars. It is known as 'synchrotron' emission, since the effect is well known on earth in the high-energy accelerating machines of nuclear physics. In (*b*) an electron is accelerated as it approaches a proton (the nucleus of the hydrogen atom). The electron pursues a hyperbolic orbit around the proton and it is not captured. During the acceleration radiation is emitted—predominantly in the short radio wave-band (the centimetre region). The process is known as a free-free transition (that is, a transition in the energy of an electron which is free, as distinct from the transitions of electrons which are captured and moving in orbit around the proton). This type of radiation is emitted in the ionised hydrogen in the plane of the Milky Way and is known as 'thermal emission'; (*c*) illustrates the radiation emitted by the neutral hydrogen gas. The hydrogen atom can be pictured as consisting of the electron moving in a nearly circular orbit around the proton. In addition to this movement around the proton the electron is spinning on its own axis. The energy of the atom depends on the direction of this spin with respect to the proton and the change in energy involved in a reversal in the direction ($l \rightarrow r$) is such that radiation is emitted on a wave-length of 21 cm. As distinct from (*a*) and (*b*) in which the energies, and hence the wave-length emitted can vary over a broad band, the energy changes in (*c*) are discrete and the radio emission occurs on a specific wave-length—or line frequency. Normally the change in the two states of the electron occurs on the average only once in 11 million years, but such vast numbers of atoms are involved in the gas clouds of the Milky Way that the emission may be measured by radio telescopes on earth.

the same direction as the nucleus, or in opposition. If the spin changes, then the energy of the atom changes, and Van der Hulst calculated that the resultant radiation should be detectable in the radio wave-band on a wave-length of 21 cm. Although such a transition would be an event of the rarest occurrence, the concentrations of neutral hydrogen in space were so immense, and involved so many trillions of atoms, that these emissions should be detectable by radio telescopes equipped with the appropriate receivers.

As soon as the war ended, the astronomers in Leiden began to devise apparatus to test this theory, simultaneously radio astronomers in Harvard and Sydney started on the same task. Although the problem presented extreme technical difficulty, by 1951 all three groups succeeded in measuring this emission on 21 cm. within a few weeks of one another.

The discovery has been one of the greatest importance, for not only have the radio telescopes penetrated to the gas clouds which are obscured by the dust between earth and the central region of the galaxy, but they have measured with precision the spiral nature of the Milky Way. It has been shown that the gas is not spread evenly through the plane, but forms long lanes, or spiral arms. These are roughly 6,000 light-years apart, and are wound tightly round the core of the galaxy. The speed of movement at the ends of the arms is twice as great as the speed of rotation of the material in the centre. The interstellar hydrogen gas is therefore in motion with respect to the observer on earth and a Doppler effect is produced on the 21-cm. wave-length neutral hydrogen emission. The radiation reaching the earth differs in wave-length from the 21 cm. emitted by the gas in space. The effect has a well-known analogy in sound—for example, the change in pitch of a train as it moves through a station where a listener stands.

In the latter case the variation occurs in sound waves, and the change in pitch is due to the relative motion of the train and the observer. In the case of the hydrogen atoms, we are dealing with radio waves, not sound waves, but the effect is analogous and the change in the measured frequency arises because the hydrogen atoms in the gas clouds are in motion with respect to the solar system, and hence with respect to the observer on earth. As the emitted radio waves remain precisely on the calculated frequency of 1,420·40 megacycles per sec., if the actual frequency at which they are received on earth is determined, it is possible to find out how fast and in what direction these hydrogen clouds are moving with respect to the solar system. The results of these observations have revealed clearly the spiral formation of the galaxy and confirm the similarity of the large-scale structure of the Milky Way with that of the extra-galactic spiral nebulae.

For a long time, although stars could clearly be seen in the spiral arms of galaxies, little detail could be seen in the central regions. During the war, Professor W. Baade, taking advantage of the black-out in Los Angeles, used the

A spiral nebula so situated in space that it can be photographed 'face on' from earth.
This photograph, taken with the 200-in. telescope, shows clearly the arrangement
of the stars in the spiral arms radiating from the dense nucleus. The Milky Way
system would look like this if photographed from a distant point in the universe.
This photograph is of the spiral nebula M51 in Canes Venatica. This nebula is
10 to 15 million light-years away and is receding from us at the rate of 300 miles
per sec. The nebula is of particular interest for two reasons. First, it was the
nebula of which Lord Rosse made a drawing, clearly depicting the spiral structure,
in the eighteenth century with the help of his 72-in. telescope. Second, the nebula
is joined by a tenuous arm to a smaller nebula. Many thousands of such multiple
systems are now known. It is possible that such galaxies have become physically
associated as they approach one another in the dense clusters.

103

100-in. Mt Wilson telescope to photograph the nucleus of the Andromeda nebula. He began in 1943, using blue-sensitive plates of high speed, and at last found signs of the beginning of resolution. No further progress was possible so he turned to red-sensitive plates, with improved speed and long exposure, although, unless the unresolved stars were themselves red, no result would be expected. He used exposure times of 4 hours, during which the focus might change by more than 1 minute because of the cooling of the secondary mirror in the night air. An accurate method had to be devised to compensate for these changes of focus. The resulting successful photographic plates showed that the resolution into stars had been achieved. The brightest stars were red giants of the same kind as the brightest stars in globular clusters in our galaxy. They were of a different type from those predominantly blue stars commonly photographed in the spiral arms of the galaxy. The stars in the central regions of the galaxies discovered by Baade are known to be old stars existing in regions where star formation has largely ceased. Baade christened these stars Population II. The blue stars, still in the process of formation, found in the spiral arms, are known as Population I. The hot stars of the spiral arms burn up so rapidly that their lifetime is 50–100 million years. The fact that such stars are always present in spirals means that new ones must always be replacing the old.

The relative amount of hydrogen gas to stars in the central regions is very low, compared with the proportion in the spiral arms. Oort has estimated that within 30 light-years of the galactic centre, the density of material in the Milky Way system is 24,000 times greater than the density near the sun. This is almost entirely due to the great concentrations of stars in these central regions, whereas near the sun in the spiral arms, 30,000 light-years from the centre, the hydrogen contributes $\frac{1}{5}$ of the total mass, in these central regions the contribution from the hydrogen gas is only $\frac{1}{400}$.

A remarkable discovery has recently been made by the Leiden astronomers about the gas in these central regions. At a distance from the centre of about 6,000 light-years there appears to be a dense arm taking part in the rotation of the galactic system with a velocity of 120 miles per sec. The unexpected feature is that the hydrogen gas in this arm seems to be moving radially away from the centre with a speed of more than 30 miles per sec. At this rate of streaming in a time of 1,000 or 2,000 million years the central regions would become entirely devoid of gas. This gas may be replenished from the galactic corona, or, as suggested by the Russian astronomer, Academician V. A. Ambartzumian, from matter in some entirely unknown state. The reason for the expansion and the mode of replenishment is at present an interesting and important problem.

2. THE RADIO EMISSION FROM THE IONISED HYDROGEN GAS

The radio waves which originate in the ionised hydrogen gas can be received over a wide range of wave-lengths—unlike the spectral line emissions from the neutral hydrogen which is on the specific wave-length of 21 cm. The radiation emitted by stars is absorbed by the hydrogen in their vicinity which becomes ionised—the electron in the atom having been ejected away from the proton, so that both then exist as separate entities. Near hot stars clouds of hydrogen are fully ionised, and when these free electrons pass close to the field of a proton, an interaction occurs without the electron being captured by the proton. This is known as a free-free transition, and the radiation which results is emitted, not as light, but on a long wave-length in the radio wave part of the spectrum.

It is believed that radio waves received from the neighbourhood of the galactic plane at short wave-lengths, 10 cm. or so, are predominantly generated by this free-free transition effect. This is commonly known as thermal radiation.

3. THE SYNCHROTRON RADIO EMISSION

On longer wave-lengths (in the metre wave-band) the peak of intensity near the galactic plane is believed to arise from a process suggested by the Russian astronomer Professor I. S. Shklovsky. The free electrons in the galaxy move in the galactic magnetic field. There is a well-known principle in physics according to which radiation occurs when electrons are accelerated to velocities near that of light in a magnetic field. This is known as synchrotron emission. Shklovsky suggested that synchrotron emission was occurring in the galaxy on a vast scale because the free electrons in the galaxy were moving at high speed in the galactic magnetic field, the emission occurring in the radio part of the spectrum. This source of radiation predominates on long radio wave-lengths not only in the galactic plane, but also as a halo or corona of emission surrounding and enclosing the entire galactic system. In the intermediate wave-length range (50 cm.–1 m.) both thermal and synchrotron emission make significant contributions.

4. THE LOCALISED SOURCES OF RADIO EMISSION
IN THE GALAXY

In addition there are several localised or discrete sources of radio emission in the plane of the Milky Way revealed by surveys made with large radio telescopes. These are now almost all identified. The first source to be found was an object relatively close to us, only 4,000 light-years away from the solar system, well inside our own galaxy, and consisting of the remains of a star which blew up—a supernova explosion. The explosion was seen and recorded in the year A.D. 1054 by the Chinese astronomers, and the remnants are known as the Crab nebula. At the time when this event took place, all the material of the star blew up, a tremendous hydrogen bomb explosion involving not just a few pounds of hydrogen but all the trillions of tons comprising the star. When this occured a star, invisible one night, became as bright as Venus and then gradually faded

The Crab nebula photographed by the 200-in. Mt Palomar telescope. This is the most
famous case of a gigantic stellar explosion—a supernova—in which the entire star
disintegrates. This event was observed by Chinese astronomers in A.D. 1054, when
a star as bright as Jupiter suddenly appeared in the constellation of Taurus
where previously there had been no star visible to the naked eye. This photograph
shows the gaseous remains which are still expanding at the rate of 70 million
miles a day. The nebula is in the Milky Way comparatively close to us—4,100
light-years distant. Although the Chinese astronomers recorded the supernova in
A.D. 1054, the actual disintegration of the star must have occurred 4,100 years
earlier, since the light from the nebula takes this time on its journey through space
to us. Thus the star actually exploded in about 3046 B.C. This supernova remnant
is the third strongest radio source in the sky. The radio waves are believed to be
generated by the synchrotron process—that is, the electrons in the nebula are
spiralling at high speed around the magnetic lines of force.

away. A thousand years later we see the supernova as a region of streaming gas with the gaseous shell expanding at the rate of 78 million miles a day. This object appears to be the third strongest source of radio emission in the sky. It has a magnetic field and as the electrons are accelerated to very high energies synchrotron radiation is emitted similar to that from the disk and halo of the galaxy. Discoveries by scientists in Russia and Leiden that both the light and radio emission from the nebula is polarised, support these theories that the magnetic field plays a prominent part in the processes taking place in the Crab nebula.

Was it possible that other discrete sources of radio emission were also supernova remnants? There appeared to be two classes of these sources—first, a concentration lying in the galactic plane, and, second, those which seemed to be distributed isotropically over the sky. The latter are now known to lie far beyond the confines of the Milky Way and will be discussed in Chapter 9.

The former are all objects contained within the Milky Way. It is hard to classify them with certainty as supernova remnants, for the only other well-authenticated cases of stars exploding were those observed by Tycho Brahe in 1572 and Kepler in 1604. Radio sources were found to be coincident with both of these supernova remnants.

The strongest source of radio emission lies in the constellation of Cassiopeia, and is not obviously related to any prominent visual object. When the position of this source was determined with sufficient accuracy this region of the sky was photographed by Baade and Minkowski with the 200-in. Mt Palomar telescope, and an extremely faint nebulosity was found, containing filaments of gas in violent internal motion. It was concluded that the object was a supernova remnant not recorded in astronomical annals.

The famous Cygnus loop, or Veil nebula in Cygnus, is another object in the galaxy believed to be the expanding gaseous shell of a supernova. If the present velocity of expansion of this shell is projected back in time it is concluded that the explosion of the star took place 50,000 years ago. Radio isophotes obtained with a high definition radio telescope correlate closely with the filamentary parts of this nebula which are unobscured by dust. This fact gives further support to the contention that many of the discrete sources of radio emission in the galaxy are supernova-like objects.

[*continued on page* 110]

The northern part of the filamentary nebula in Cygnus (the Veil nebula) photographed by the 100-in. Mt Wilson telescope. The bright star at the top of the photograph is 52 Cygni. Photographs of a greater area of sky in this region indicate that there are two wisps of this nebulous cloud, separated by about 3°, apparently forming two parts of a circle. If the circle joining these two nebulous arcs were to be completed it would enclose a region of fifty light-years of space. It is thought that these gaseous arcs are expanding from a point near the centre of this region, and that they are the remains of a supernova explosion which occurred 50,000 years ago.

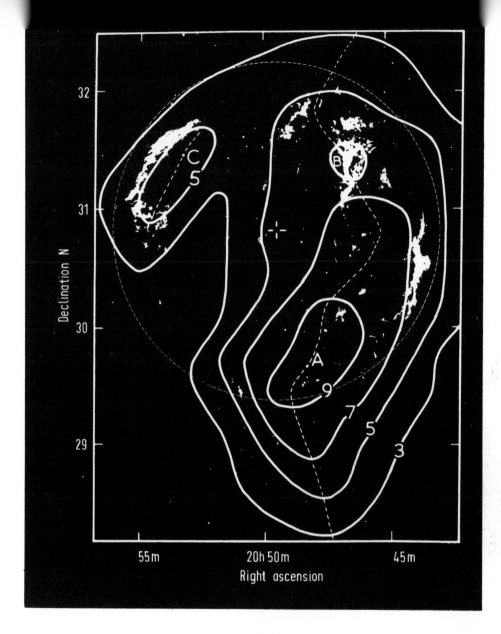

The possibility that the Veil nebula in Cygnus is formed from the gaseous remains of a supernova explosion lends great interest to the investigation of the radio emission from this part of the sky. This illustration shows the contours of the radio emission obtained with the Jodrell Bank telescope superimposed on a photograph of the sky containing all the gaseous filaments associated with the nebula. The numbers on the isophotes represent the relative strength of the radio emission. The northern part of the nebula illustrated opposite is the filament on the right of this photograph. It will be seen that there is a good correlation between the isophotes and the gaseous filaments, particularly in the parts marked (*B*) and (*C*), although the most intense radio emission is centred on the southern region marked (*A*) near one of the fainter areas of the nebula. Close inspection of the photographs, however, shows that in this region the filaments have a markedly striated pattern.

Population II stars, the ancient stars, are found in the nuclear regions of the galaxies where little of the interstellar gas remains. Population I stars, on the other hand, are the young stars, to be found wherever concentrations of hydrogen gas exist, particularly in the spiral arms of the galaxies.

Here in these nebulous clouds are small, dark spherical objects, only a light-year or less in diameter, which may represent the early stages of star formation. A slight disturbance in the huge mass of hydrogen gas may have started the condensation of the globules, which continues under the gravitational force of the mass of gas, and is assisted by the radiation pressure of surrounding starlight. More and more energy is liberated as the globule contracts and its temperature rises, until radiation, first in the infra-red, and then the visible part of the spectrum commences. Then the central regions of this condensing mass become so hot that thermo-nuclear reactions occur, and the long process begins, lasting for thousands of millions of years, by which the hydrogen will be gradually converted to helium. When the supply of hydrogen is exhausted, the star will begin to collapse, and become a white dwarf.

Our own sun is well established in the hydrogen-helium conversion phase, its original globule having begun to form in the primeval hydrogen gas 10,000 million years ago, so that half of the original hydrogen has already been exhausted. Whilst the remaining hydrogen continues to burn, the sun can remain in a state of equilibrium for about another 5,000–6,000 million years. When all reserves are exhausted there can be no further production of energy by thermo-nuclear processes to balance the gravitational forces which are tending to pull the remaining gas together. The sun will then begin to collapse, and pressure will build up to such an extent that even more energy will be generated, and expansion will begin. For the subsequent million years while its thermo-nuclear processes are ceasing, any civilisations which still exist in the solar system would vanish under rapidly changing conditions. The temperature of the earth would begin to increase at the rate of about $10°$ every million years, so that eventually all the oceans would boil and the sun itself become so inflated that it occupied most of the space of the solar system. When all reserves of energy had finally disappeared and nothing further was left capable of transformation to produce energy, then the final collapse would take place, leading to the condition of a white dwarf.

This picture of the possible trend of a star's evolution is a very simplified one. In some cases catastrophes happen which give rise to supernovae like the Crab nebula. In this case heavy elements which have already been formed in a star are ejected into space and probably absorbed in the interstellar clouds where new stars are beginning to form. The interstellar hydrogen contains the scatterings of heavy elements from stars whose lives were ended long ago in a supernova

[continued on page 113]

DROMEDA NEBULA photographed in blue shows giant and super-giant stars of ULATION I in the spiral arms. The hazy ɲ at the upper left is composed of solved Population II stars.

NGC 205, companion of the Andromeda Nebula, photographed in yellow light shows stars of **POPULATION II**. The brightest stars are red and 100 times fainter than the blue giants of Population I.

The very bright, uniformly distributed stars in both pictures are foreground stars belonging in our own Milky Way system.

The stars are generally divided into two broad groups, according to their age and position in the galaxies. The Population I stars are associated with regions containing dust and gas where stars are still in process of formation. These are the young stars and are particularly prominent in the spiral arms of galaxies. The sun belongs to Population I. On the other hand, the Population II stars are the old stars found in regions devoid of gas and dust where star formation has largely ceased. These stars are situated in the central regions of the spiral galaxies and are predominant in the elliptical galaxies. This photograph, taken by the 200-in. Mt Palomar telescope, shows the two populations in the Andromeda nebula, the object in which Baade first identified the nature of the stars in the central regions of the galaxy.

The Great nebula M42 in Orion photographed by the 100-in.
Mt Wilson telescope. On a clear night it is possible to see with the
naked eye a luminous patch under the three stars of Orion's belt.
In a telescope this is resolved as two luminous nebulae of gas, the
larger of which is shown here. There are many such nebulae in
the Milky Way. They consist of clouds of hydrogen gas which
have been ionised and made self-luminous by intense ultra-violet
light from near-by hot stars. In these nebulae small dark globules
may be seen, and these are believed to be the beginnings of the
condensations from which eventually stars are formed.

explosion. This would seem to explain the presence on earth, and in the planetary system, of those heavy elements which could not have been formed by the sun itself in its present stage.

In the central regions of the galaxy, where the Population II stars predominate, there is no evidence of star formation taking place. The hydrogen has vanished and the stars are old. The reasons for this are not really understood; it is a subject which belongs to the evolution of the galaxies themselves and of the cosmos as a whole.

It would appear that when our Milky Way system, M31 and the other galaxies were formed, the processes of star formation took place first in the central regions of the galaxies. Either this used up all the gas in the early history of the galaxy, or some other collisions took place which swept the remaining gas away from these central regions. Today it is only in the spiral arms, where these regions of hydrogen gas exist, that stars are being born.

9 Beyond the Milky Way

EXTRA-GALACTIC NEBULAE

The evidence provided by both optical and radio telescopes indicates that the Milky Way system is typical of many extra-galactic spiral nebulae, and very much akin to M31 in Andromeda. The photographs taken by the large optical telescopes show that great numbers of these extra-galactic nebulae exist. Many have their stars contained in a spiral formation like the Milky Way and M31, but others are relatively structureless, with the stars and gas apparently uniformly distributed throughout a spherical or ellipsoidal region. It seems probable that the many different forms of nebulae visible in the telescopes represent some evolutionary sequence but the situation is not clearly understood at the moment.

The 200-in. Mt Palomar telescope has penetrated 5,000 million light-years into space, and within this region of time and space these galaxies seem to be distributed in a fairly uniform way. Few exist alone; they are nearly all found in clusters or groups. Our own Milky Way system belongs to a small group, including the Adromeda nebula M31, about 2 million light-years away, and about a dozen others. This group occupies a space the shape of a flattened ellipsoid with a major axis of 2 million light-years. This is a small group compared with some of the well-known groups such as those in Virgo and Coma, which contain hundreds of galaxies. The telescopes so far have not shown any differences in the large-scale organisation of the universe out to the limits of their penetration, so that no changes in the past history of the universe have been revealed. As we look out into space, so we look back in time, for the light from these distant objects has taken thousands of millions of years on its journey to us on earth.

[*Opposite*]   A cluster of galaxies in the constellation of Hercules photographed by the 200-in. Mt Palomar telescope. The foreground stars of the Milky Way in this photograph are either the perfectly circular faint images or the bright diffuse spots with the diffraction cross. All the other images are of remote extra-galactic nebulae and there are at least as many of these nebulae visible in the illustration as there are foreground stars. Extra-galactic nebulae of many types are visible, including two closely interacting spiral galaxies seen face on (*lower centre*). Clusters of galaxies like this are probably the basic units of the universe which take part in the general expansion. Within the clusters the galaxies move at random under their own gravitational forces. The number of galaxies in the clusters vary enormously. The Milky Way and Andromeda are part of a small cluster of about

[*continued*] twenty-four nebulae. One of the largest known is the Coma cluster which probably contains 10,000 galaxies in a volume of about 440 million million million cubic light-years of space. Within the field of view of the 200-in. it has been estimated that the average number of galaxies in a cluster is 200 and the average diameter of the clusters about 5 million light-years.

Observations of the light reaching us from these distant galaxies has shown a reddening effect, and since 1912 when Professor Slipher at the Lowell Observatory made measurements of this, there has been much controversy about the interpretation of the phenomena. If it were the result of a Doppler effect (see Chapter 8) causing the wave-length of the light to be increased and therefore reddened, as the object moves away relative to the observer, then the velocities of these objects would be far greater than that of any known celestial body.

Hubble's observations at the Mt Wilson Observatory of the red shift in the spectrum of the light from these far galaxies led him to conclude that the extent of the shift was in direct proportion to a galaxy's distance from us, and astronomers accept that this does, indeed, indicate that the galaxies are moving apart at great speed.

At present no other reasonable explanation has been given, and the interpretation implies that the galaxies are all moving away from one another with increasing speed as they move farther apart. At the present-day limit of penetration of the 200-in. telescope—the cluster of galaxies in Boötes at a distance of

[*Opposite*] In 1917 Slipher photographed the spectra of the light from some of the extra-galactic nebulae. In principle the spectrum is similar to that of a star (or the sun); that is, continuous from the blue to the red, but crossed by absorption lines arising from elements which can be identified from their spectrum observed in the laboratory. Slipher found, to his surprise, that the absorption lines in some of these photographs of the nebulae were displaced towards the red end of the spectrum. If this shift were interpreted as a shift due to the motion of the galaxies away from the Milky Way (the Doppler effect), then the speeds of recession were very high. In 1929 Hubble discovered that this shift (which he interpreted as a speed of recession) increased linearly with the distance of the galaxy—and this remains the situation today. This illustration shows the measurements of the spectra from clusters of galaxies at increasing distances. The vertical lines in the spectra are the comparison lines from a source in the observatory and the progressive shift to the red of the hydrogen and potassium lines is shown by the arrow. Since this illustration was compiled, the Mt Palomar telescope has measured a red shift of 46 per cent of the velocity of light—85,500 miles a second —corresponding to a distance of the cluster of 4,500 million light-years.

RELATION BETWEEN RED-SHIFT AND DISTANCE
FOR EXTRAGALACTIC NEBULAE

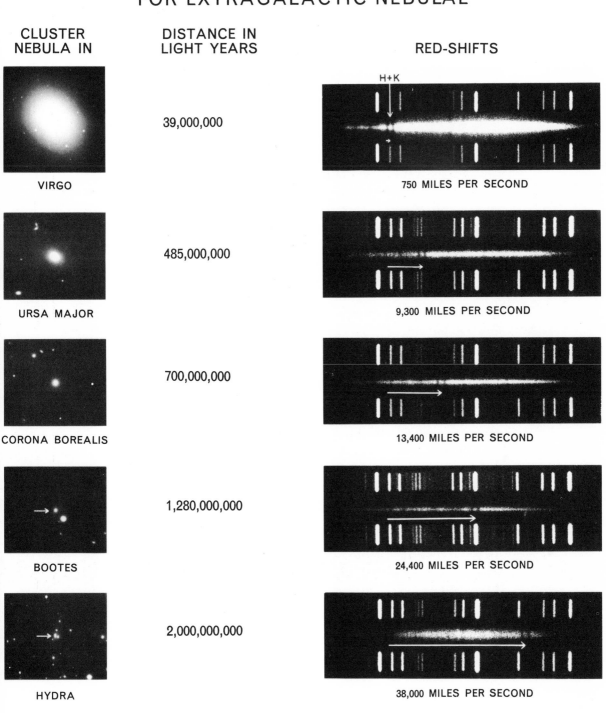

CLUSTER NEBULA IN	DISTANCE IN LIGHT YEARS	RED-SHIFTS
VIRGO	39,000,000	750 MILES PER SECOND
URSA MAJOR	485,000,000	9,300 MILES PER SECOND
CORONA BOREALIS	700,000,000	13,400 MILES PER SECOND
BOOTES	1,280,000,000	24,400 MILES PER SECOND
HYDRA	2,000,000,000	38,000 MILES PER SECOND

Red-shifts are expressed as velocities, c dλ/λ. Arrows indicate shift for calcium lines H and K. One light-year equals about 6 trillion miles, or 6×10^{12} miles.

4,500 million light-years—the shift of the spectral lines towards the red shows that the velocity of recession is 46 per cent of the velocity of light—that is, 85,500 miles per sec.

It should be mentioned here that this recession is a feature of the universe involving the clusters of galaxies, which appear to be the large-scale units of the cosmos. The individual galaxies within the clusters are in random motion under the influence of their mutual gravitational attractions and in many cases are moving towards one another—as is the case with M31 and the Milky Way.

THEORIES OF THE UNIVERSE

The observations with the telescopes of these remote epochs of space and time reveal a high degree of large-scale uniformity in the cosmos and give no clear indication of any significant changes in this overall structure during the last 5,000 million years. In fact, if we imagine the present speeds of recession to be reversed then it is simple to calculate that on this basis we would have to retrace time for about 10,000 million years in order to find an initial concentrated condition of the matter which comprises the cosmos. Since our instruments cannot penetrate to such a remote epoch it is necessary to appeal to cosmological theory in an endeavour to assess whether our present observations are indeed compatible with a beginning of the universe at this time.

a. EVOLUTIONARY THEORIES

The modern theoretical ideas in cosmology began in 1916 when Einstein explored the cosmological consequence of his theory of general relativity. In the solution of Einstein's theory of general relativity there was an arbitrary constant —the lambda term—and this caused tremendous controversy as a variety of model universes can be specified depending on the value of this constant. They have one factor in common: they represent a universe in an evolutionary state, which in time past had some degree of singularity. For example, if the cosmical constant is zero then the theory is compatible with an explosive act of creation from a superdense state 10,000 million years ago, and the expansion which we witness today is the result of the initial impetus of the explosion.

The implications of the theory if the cosmical constant is positive have been developed by the Belgian Père Lemaître. He suggested that our universe began in a very highly compressed and hot state in the form of a primeval atom, perhaps 40,000–60,000 million years ago. This atom was a concentrate of neutrons or protons so densely packed that the nuclei were squeezed together in a degenerate state. The entire mass of the universe was contained in a space no larger than that occupied by the solar system today. In this unstable condition some radioactive disintegration must have given rise to an expanding movement. So the material gradually spread out into space, and after 1,000 million years of time, the same number of light-years of space were occupied by hydrogen gas. Gravitational forces now introduced a state of stability and the universe began to settle down into a uniform distribution of primeval gas. Then condensations began to appear, as the gas aggregated into stars and galaxies. In this condition the positive cosmical constant is equivalent to a physical force working in opposition to Newtonian forces of gravitational attraction, and it is these forces which are responsible for the expanding movement we are observing now. On these evolutionary theories all the basic material in the universe was created at once, and there has been no further creation since. According to this belief, as there has been a beginning, so there must be an end.

b. THE STEADY STATE THEORY

Opposed to this is the view held by other scientists that the universe is infinite and uniform in space and time, has had neither a beginning nor will have an end. As new matter is being steadily created, the density remains constant, so that the thinning by expansion is exactly matched by this newly created material. The approach of Professors Hoyle and McCrea to this theory is mathematical, whilst Professors Bondi and Gold argue from the principle that the large-scale features of the universe are the same not only from every point of view in space, but also from every point of view in time. Hoyle has summarised the implications of the theory in this way:

'Expansion takes place in space *between* galactic systems: individual galaxies and clusters do not themselves expand. The very old material of the universe is concentrated in very old galaxies. By virtue of the universal expansion these are now extremely far apart. Possibly there are some moderately old galaxies within the range of our telescopes. If a method could be worked out to identify distant galaxies composed of comparatively old matter, it would provide a test of the steady state theory.'

THE USE OF RADIO TELESCOPES IN THE SEARCH
FOR A SOLUTION TO THE COSMOLOGICAL PROBLEM

Which theory approximates most closely to the truth, that of the evolutionary universe, with a beginning and ending in time and space, or the steady state theory, where wastage of material is constantly being replaced by the continuous creation of new hydrogen atoms? Man, even though he now possesses the wonderful new instruments described in this book, is still searching for the answer. His powerful optical telescopes provide material which the earliest astronomers can scarcely have dreamed of, and latterly his radio telescopes have begun to yield exciting possibilities relating to these cosmological problems, added to which is the data gained by the probes and satellites.

The investigation of radio emissions from the discrete sources mentioned in Chapter 8 shows that although the distribution of thousands of these sources is

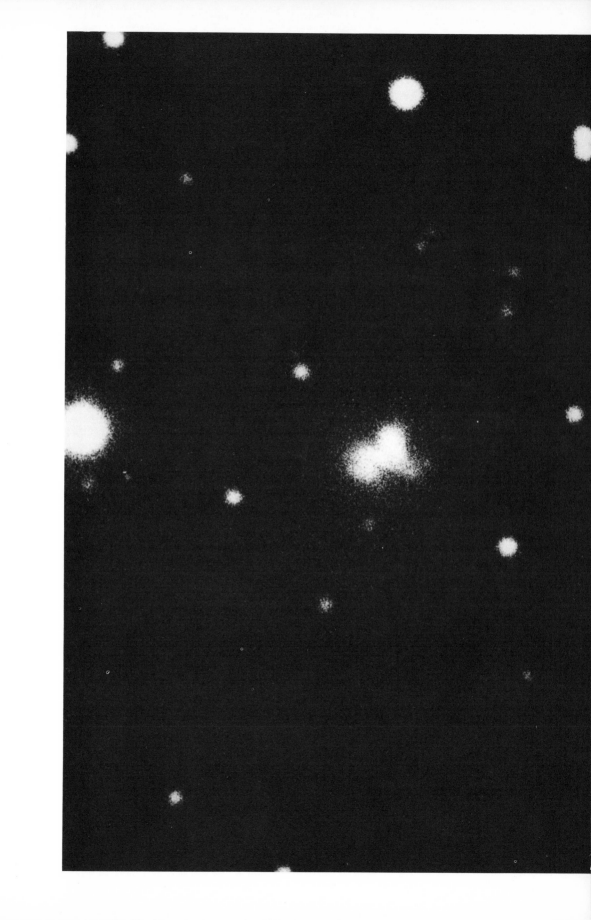

isotropic, yet there are only very few, like M31, which can be linked with individual extra-galactic nebulae. In fact, even with the most powerful radio telescopes only two or three dozen individual extra-galactic nebulae have been identified as radio sources. In the case of M31 high resolution surveys have shown the presence of a corona or halo of radio emission surrounding this galaxy, as in the case of the Milky Way system. There is some evidence that more distant spirals are similarly enclosed. The discovery of these radio coronae has shown that the galaxies do not exist in isolation, but as complex entities, consisting not only of the gas and dust of interstellar space but also of high-speed electrons accelerated in the magnetic fields of the galaxies and producing the corona, hidden from the optical telescopes, but revealed by the radio telescopes.

However, these radio studies of the individual extra-galactic nebulae do not solve the major problem of the identity of the thousands of radio sources which are distributed isotropically. They cannot be contained in the Milky Way system, otherwise they would be concentrated in the plane of the system, and only a few of them can be linked up with the normal extra-galactic nebulae.

An indication of a possible solution to this problem came when the second strongest radio source in the sky—in the constellation of Cygnus—was identified. This source, like Cassiopeia, is close to the galactic plane, but whereas the Cassiopeia source was identified with a supernova remnant, no such galactic object could be found which might give rise to the emission from Cygnus. In 1951 Dr F. G. Smith in Cambridge, using a radio interferometer of high resolving power, defined the position of the source within an area of 1 sq. minute of arc. Baade and Minkowski then used the 200-in. Mt Palomar telescope to make a very long exposure of this area of sky. The result was surprising. What had appeared on the plates of smaller telescopes as a single galaxy was now shown to be two spiral

[*Opposite*]   The photography of this part of the sky in Cygnus using exposures of many hours with the 200-in. Mt Palomar telescope was stimulated by the presence there of the second strongest radio source in the heavens, which did not seem to be related to any particularly outstanding photographic object. However, the 200-in. photograph revealed the strange event depicted in the centre of this illustration. The interpretation made by the Mt Palomar astronomers Walter Baade and Rudolph Minkowski from the original negative was that the object consisted of two spiral nebulae closely interacting— apparently in a state of collision. The great distance—550 million light-years —coupled with the anomaly that the object was faint optically but a strong emitter of radio waves, led to the belief that many of the unidentified radio sources were peculiar objects of this type, so remote that they were beyond the range of the 200-in. telescope.

galaxies, one superimposed on the other. They were in close contact, with the nuclei strongly distorted by gravitational interaction. The centres were only about 2 seconds of arc apart, indicating that they had penetrated far into one another. In spite of this, it is unlikely that individual stars would have actually collided, as the distances between them are so immense. Their gravitational attraction would distort to a certain extent the structure of the galaxy, so that there would be considerable effects upon the clouds of dust and gas. The particles in these clouds would collide at speeds of thousands of miles per second, so that the gas would be heated to temperatures of tens of millions of degrees.

Examination of the spectrum of light from this hot material, in which the atoms were in a highly excited state, made it possible to measure the red shift, and so calculate the distance of these interacting galaxies from us—550 million light-years. Such an event as this close interaction or collision must be exceedingly rare, and the fact that it can be observed by the radio astronomer is of the utmost importance. The source is so strong that it could be detected by present instruments even if it were only 1/3,000 as intense, which means that it would be possible to detect such events at distances far beyond the range of the 200-in. telescope. These investigations are of great importance to those engaged in cosmological problems, since the observations at such distances mean that the universe is observed in a remote epoch. The past history of the universe, far beyond the range of the optical telescopes, may at last be studied. Some astronomers do not accept the view that the galaxies in Cygnus are colliding. The Russian astronomer Ambartzumian maintains that the object is the nucleus of a galaxy dividing to form two separate galaxies. In some recent theoretical discussions doubt has been expressed as to whether the intensity of the radio

[continued on page 126]

[*Opposite*] Another remote and peculiar object, photographed with the 200-in. which has been identified as a source of strong radio emission. This object, which is in Centaurus, is also believed to be an example of two closely interacting or colliding galaxies. The dark rift is caused by the obscuration of the light by the interstellar dust of the galaxies. For many years it has been widely accepted that the act of collision in which the dust and gas (but not the stars) collided at high speed was the basic cause of the intense radio emission. In 1962, however, serious doubt was cast on this interpretation, because the energy involved in such collisions seemed insufficient to explain the intensity of the radio output. There is no generally accepted theory, although one suggestion is that the peculiar objects of this type might be in a state of evolution in which abnormal numbers of supernova explosions occur. Since it is known from the study of the radio sources in the Milky Way that supernova remnants are powerful sources of radio waves (see Chapter 8) it would be possible to account for the intensity of the radio emission from the distant objects by postulating a sufficient number of supernova.

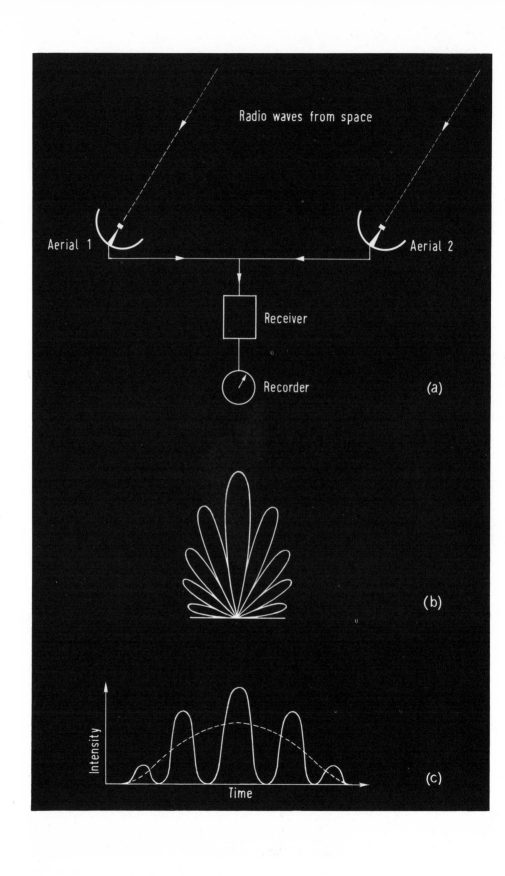

Radio waves from space

Aerial 1

Aerial 2

Receiver

Recorder

(a)

(b)

Intensity

Time

(c)

[*Opposite*]   Amongst the specialised forms of radio telescope developed for specific problems is the interferometer. In its simplest form this consists of two radio telescopes separated along the ground but connected to a common receiver and recorder as shown in (*a*). Instead of the single beam of the individual aerials, the reception pattern of the combined pair is a system of lobes as shown in (*b*). The angle between the successive maxima or minima decreases as the separation of the aerials is increased. If such an aerial combination is swept across a part of the sky containing a radio source whose angular dimensions are less than this angle between the lobes then the recorded signal strength will go through a series of maxima and minima as shown in (*c*), whereas from one aerial alone the response would be broad as shown by the broken line. The two aerials are often fixed and the motion of the earth is allowed to sweep the lobe pattern across the radio source. The precision with which the central lobe can be identified makes it possible to determine the position of the radio source in the sky far more accurately than with a single broad beam.

[*Below*]   Developments of the basic interferometer arrangement shown opposite have had important applications in radio astronomy. One such application which has been significant in cosmological studies is the measurement of the diameter of the radio sources. The principle of this technique is illustrated in the diagram. Suppose the two aerials of the interferometer are positioned so that the lobes are separated as shown in (*a*), and imagine that we have two radio sources: (S_1) whose angular diameter is small compared with the angular separation of the lobes, and (S_2) whose angular diameter is larger than the lobe separation. If the earth sweeps the interferometer pattern across these sources then the response from (S_1) will be as shown in (*b*); that is, it will exhibit the full extent of the maxima and minima. The response from (S_2) will be as shown in (*c*), where the 'fringe' amplitude is much reduced because it is never completely separated by the individual lobes. If the sources have the same intensity then the mean response (which would be obtained by one aerial alone) will be the same as shown by the broken lines in (*b*) and (*c*). Since the angle between the fringes depends only on the wave-length and the physical separation of the aerials it is known accurately. If the amplitude of the fringe patterns from the same source is observed at a number of spacings it is possible to calculate the angular diameter of the source.

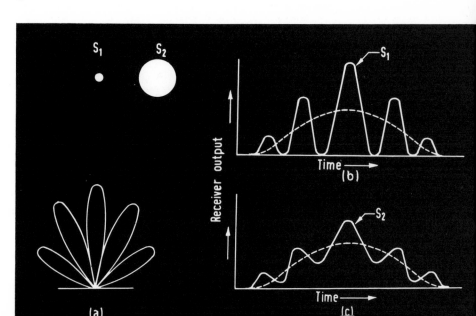

waves from interacting galaxies like Cygnus have in fact anything to do with the collision itself. Even the great energies involved in such a collision are insufficient to account for the radio emission—but no satisfactory source of the energy has yet been suggested. In any case, both in this and subsequent discoveries of distant radio sources, the important factor is that certain processes are taking place, at huge distances of time and space, which produce a large output of energy in the radio wave part of the spectrum.

Telescopes designed especially to receive these emissions consist of aerials separated sometimes by many miles. Instead of the single beam of the parabolic reflector, the combined aerials form a system of lobes. Using this and similar techniques, Professor Ryle in Cambridge, and radio astronomers in Sydney, Australia, have investigated the distribution of thousands of these sources. The Cambridge observations show a good agreement between the distribution of these objects through space and their radio and optical intensity, but for very weak sources (presumably at great distances) the numbers appear to be greater than would be indicated by a concept of uniform distribution in space and time. The simplest interpretation of this result is that the spatial density of the

[*Opposite*]   Two examples of the measurement of the angular diameter of a radio source. These interferometer records were obtained by combining the signals received in the 250-ft. Jodrell Bank telescope with those received in a smaller radio telescope which could be moved at various distances from Jodrell Bank. The records for each source are shown at four different base-lines or separations between the two radio telescopes—reading from top to bottom 2·5 miles, 11 miles, 37 miles, 70 miles. At the longest base-line the signal from the remote station was transmitted back to Jodrell Bank via two radio links. In the case of the source on the left (Source 1) the amplitude of the fringes does not decrease significantly even at the maximum separation. (The apparent decrease appears because the gain is less in the long base-line records—the 'noise level' before and after the fringes is less.) From this fact it may be deduced that the angular diameter of this source must be less than 1 second of arc. On the other hand, in the case of the right-hand records (Source 2) the fringe amplitude has decreased markedly even at the 37-mile separation. At the 70-mile separation the fringes are scarcely discernible, even although the noise level is much higher than in the 37-mile record. A detailed study of this radio source from these records indicates that its diameter must be between 3 and 10 seconds of arc—probably a central source of 3 seconds diameter surrounded by a halo of 10 seconds of arc diameter.

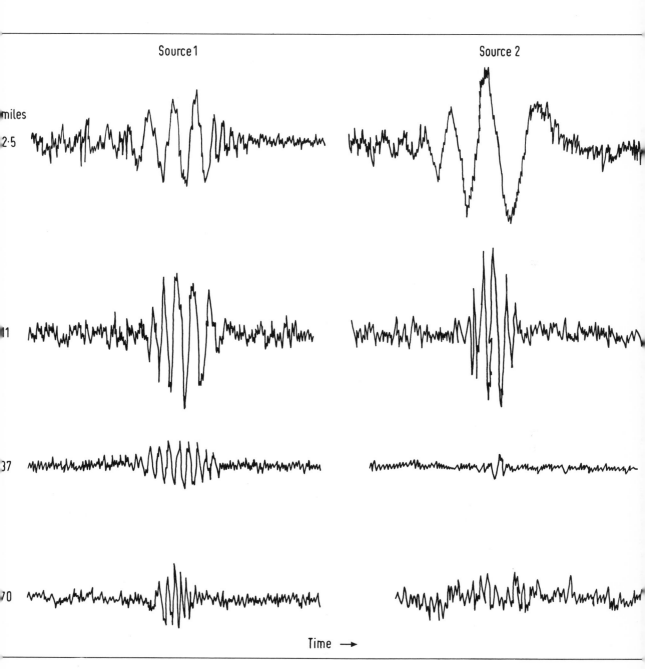

Source 1   Source 2

miles

2·5

1

37

70

Time ⟶

material of the universe, that is the number of galaxies or number of radio sources per unit volume of space, is greater in those remote parts than in regions closer to us in space and time. If this were so, for the first time we should begin to learn something of a change in the organisation of the cosmos as we penetrate farther into space and farther back in time.

The work of the radio astronomers in Sydney has yielded a different result, showing no departure from the uniform distribution out to the limits of penetration of the radio telescopes. There has been considerable criticism of the treatment of the radio source counts in this statistical manner, and to overcome this criticism the Jodrell Bank telescope has been used to obtain details about the individual sources by using it in conjunction with smaller aerials which can be moved to varying distances from it. One-third of its working time during the first four years of use was spent on this problem. Information from aerials in the remote stations—up to 70 miles away—is transmitted over a radio link, and correlated with signals picked up at the same time by the Jodrell Bank telescope. The investigation of the strength of the radio waves from the radio sources with this arrangement enables their angular diameters to be measured. By this method information is obtained from which the effective temperature of the source may be calculated, and some idea of the scale of distance arrived at. The spacing of the distant aerial is changed until the lobe separation is so small that the maximum and minimum in the interferometer fringe pattern of a particular source begin to disappear. The source is then beginning to be resolved, and it has been possible to estimate the angular diameter of the emitting region down to diameters of less than 1 second of arc.

Out of 300 of the most intense unidentified sources believed to be at distances of cosmical significance, only 10 per cent have angular diameters, indicating they are at distances greater than 2,000 million light-years. Three have angular diameters less than a second of arc, indicating that their distance from us is so tremendous that the radio waves have been on their journey to earth for 7,000 or 8,000 million years. As mentioned earlier, the cluster of galaxies in Boötes at present represents the greatest distance to which the Mt Palomar telescope has penetrated, 4,500 million light-years, where the speed of recession, measured by the red shift, is 85,500 miles per sec. The co-operation between optical telescopes and radio telescopes which this work on the distant radio sources involved, meant that within a few years the ultimate range of the Mt Palomar telescope was increased threefold.

These studies have confirmed the belief that many of the unidentified radio sources are dense clusters of galaxies, at great distances from us. The radio emissions are relatively intense because interactions or collisions—like the Cygnus event—must be occurring in these clusters. The processes by which these sources emit radio waves, which are more intense than would be anticipated from the energy in the optical part of the spectrum, is not understood. It must in some way be related to the interaction of the gas and the dust in the nebulae, and the magnetic forces are almost certainly involved. Many years of work lie ahead before the details can be unravelled, but in the meantime the existence of these sources has given rise to a new hope that the radio telescopes may now be exploring those regions of time and space which hold the key to the problem of the origin and evolution of the universe.

Acknowledgements

Grateful acknowledgement is made to many individuals and organisations for supplying several of the photographs and for permission to reproduce them in this book. Particularly to the Mt Wilson and Palomar Observatories for the photographs of the Hale and Schmidt telescopes (pages 13, 16, 17), and for the photographs of the stars and nebulae on pages 19, 61, 65, 68, 48, 98, 99, 103, 106, 108, 111, 112, 115, 117, 120, 123; to the Director of the U.S. National Radio Astronomy Observatory, West Virginia, for the photograph on page 23; to Mrs Curran, the American Consul in Manchester, for the photographs of Dr Goddard and the Pioneer rocket (page 37) and the diagram of the proposed lunar launching (page 79); to the Meteorological Satellite Laboratory of the U.S. Weather Bureau for the Tiros photographs on pages 52, 53; to the Academy of Sciences of the U.S.S.R. for the Lunik photographs on pages 58, 59, 60; to the U.S. National Aeronautics and Space Administration and the Jet Propulsion Laboratory for the Mariner II illustrations (page 66); to the Royal Astronomical Society for the solar photographs on pages 88, 89, 90, 91; to the Director of the Lick Observatory for the comet photograph (page 87). The following copyright acknowledgements are also made. Coronelli's celestial globe (frontispiece) and Newton's reflecting telescope (page 11), Crown copyright, Science Museum, London; Jodrell Bank radio telescope (page 26), the aerial tower, electric motor rotating the bowl (page 29), rack used for elevating the bowl, trunnion bearing carrying the bowl, 'cable twisting' arrangement (page 30), the control room (page 31), top section of the tower (page 33), Crown copyright, Central Office of Information; Jodrell Bank telescope, the reverse of the bowl (page 27), Rowland King & Co., Oldham; Jodrell Bank, constructing the bowl (page 28), Studio Star, Stockport; Helicopter removing apparatus from the bowl (page 33), Associated Newspapers Ltd; V-2 rocket (page 37), Imperial War Museum; Surveyor space craft (page 69), Hughes Aircraft Company; Colonel Glenn's capsule arriving at the Science Museum (page 75), *The Times*; a group of international scientists at Jodrell Bank (page 67), *The Guardian*.

List of Illustrations

Index